CAPTIONS AND GRAPHICS FOR
LOW BUDGET VIDEO

For Lesley, Zoë and Talitha, also to Spistache.

Thanks too to:
Bobby Cohen-Lax for the use of his 'Kosher' titles.
Staedtler-Mars for the photograph of their drawing board.
Margaret Riley, for patience then nagging me.

CAPTIONS AND GRAPHICS FOR LOW BUDGET VIDEO

Robin Blythe-Lord

FOCAL PRESS

Focal Press
An imprint of Butterworth-Heinemann Ltd
Linacre House, Jordan Hill, Oxford OX2 8DP

PART OF REED INTERNATIONAL BOOKS

OXFORD LONDON BOSTON
MUNICH NEW DELHI SINGAPORE SYDNEY
TOKYO TORONTO WELLINGTON

First published 1992

© Butterworth-Heinemann 1992

British Library Cataloguing in Publication Data
Blythe-Lord, Robin
    Captions and Graphics for Low Cost Video
    I. Title
    778.59
ISBN 0 2405 1312 6

Library of Congress Cataloguing in Publication Data
Blythe-Lord, Robin.
    Captions and graphics for low budget video/Robin Blythe-Lord.
    p.   cm.
    Includes index.
    ISBN 0 2405 1312 6
    1. Video tapes – Editing. 2. Television programs – Titling.
    I. Title.
    TR899.B58   1992
    77.59'92–dc20

                                                                92–770
                                                                CIP

Printed and bound in Great Britain by Redwood Press, Melksham, Wiltshire

Contents

Introduction   1

1 Copying   3
  Copy lighting   3
    Even lighting   3
    Directional lighting   7
  Exposure methods   10
  Polarizing filters   11
  Copying transparencies   14
    Slides   14
    Glowing lines and text   15
    Photographing a video screen   16
  A basic caption stand   20
  Copystand construction   21

2 Text and Layout   24
  Colour   24
    Colour and mood   25
    Contrast   27
  Grids   28
  Proportions and useful working sizes   28
  Typefaces   30
    Suitable styles for video   30
    Matching typestyle to programme   31
  Lettering and typesetting methods   34

3 Illustration   37
  Illustration for video   37
  Graphics equipment and materials   39
    Basic equipment   39
    Basic materials   46
  Photographs   49
  Sources of illustrations   49

4 Mechanicals   50
  Belt titlers   50
  Books   51
    How to bind a simple book for turning in shot   51
    Turning-page effect   55
  Magnetics   57

Paper engineering 60
  Pivots 61
  Animated card graphic 61
Rotating captions 65
  Turntables 65
  Disc 77
  Drum 78
  Cube 81
  Vane titler 82
Sand and powder captions 83
  Wet, scratched in and built up. Wash away 83
  Dry blow away, 3D reveal and adhesive reveal 83
Sliders 85
  Simple slider 85
  Sliding reveal 86
  Universal slider 87
Velcro boards 88
Models 89

5 Opticals 90
Animatics 90
Filters 92
  Diffusion filter 92
  Part colour filter 93
  Multiple image 93
  Star filter 96
Mirrors 97
  Mirror wipe 98
  Kaleidoscope 98
  Mirror tube 98
  Two-way mirrors 100
  Title on mirrors 101
  Anamorphic mirrors 103
Out of focus 104
Fluid ripple 105
Graffiti 105
Melting and dissolving captions 105

C&G Suppliers List 111

Index 121

Introduction

As you sit by your TV and watch electronic expertise being used to fold, wrap and float away an image while text is interleaved and animated you could be excused for thinking that this is all very wonderful but completely beyond your means to emulate.

And you would probably be right. But this does not mean that interesting, exciting and relevant captions or graphics are quite beyond your reach.

No, this book will not enable you to produce effects like those obtainable from Quantel Paintboxes, Harrys, Harriets, Flairs, or Astons. These are extremely sophisticated, dedicated computers, cost an awful lot to do what they do and do it very well. (Though you might be excused for wondering about the often trivial application of high technology.)

Usually the low budget user must rely either upon built-in camera titling effects or a domestic quality character generator or use the effects supplied on a vision mixer. These tend to be of limited typestyle, quality and use. They certainly will not be suitable for every programme you will make.

A lot of wonderful things are being done in the field of electronic graphics for the low budget video market. Manufacturers and suppliers such as Maze Technology have developed excellent software and hardware packages, mostly developed around PC or Amiga computers. It is possible to buy clip art discs, font discs, painting and frame grabbing packages as well as genlock systems which would have been thought a very remote possibility even two years ago. Such is the pace of technological change.

Wonderful and useful as these are, they are only tools. Obviously they are expensive. A glance through any price list and you will discover that the final cost of all the components necessary for a decent graphics and titling system is quite high. Even then the definition is unlikely to be as good as the direct optically shot portions of the tape, and can suffer from various idiosyncratic frame jitters and pronounced colour smearing. Some of the more complex effects can take what seems like geological aeons to be processed by the CPU, even with an accelerator board added.

What is important to realise is that even with all the fonts and image manipulation tools at your disposal, the basic design decisions remain exactly the same. The advice in this book regarding text, graphics, layout and relevance to your programme remains true, whatever medium is used to produce the visual.

Captions and graphics are an important integral part of a programme. While they are obviously necessary for conveying information, their potential for establishing a mood and stimulating the audience is not always appreciated or fully exploited.

You may not consider yourself to be a great artist or graphic designer, yet there are simple and effective practical techniques that, in basic form, can be easily acquired. Combined with fundamental design principles, imagination and sensitivity they can give a video production an enhanced quality and personal style.

All the techniques described in this book are simple and satisfying small projects to build and you will not need highly developed manipulative skills or specialist equipment to undertake them.

You should soon get a feel for the lateral ingenuity that is so useful in helping to solve your design and construction problems. Try to look deeper into the 'How To' description to see the aim and the principles being used. See if you can do it another way that is more straightforward for you and your circumstances. There is no completely right or wrong way; if it works efficiently and the results on screen are exactly what you hoped for, or better, and it communicates precisely, then you have produced an effective design solution.

With some sensitivity towards the programme content and objectives, some ingenuity, imagination, a little skill and some luck then wonderful things can happen for you. And all this using established principles, available technology and a bit of video magic.

1 Copying

Most of the work in this book will involve the recording of text or pictures; this is often called 'artwork', a term derived from the printing industry to denote an original, whatever it was, which was going to be copied and printed. The actual act of recording the artwork is usually called copying and has certain basic principles that need to be followed to ensure its successful outcome. Occasionally the artwork will be supported on a moving belt, roller or drum but the basic principles for lighting, exposure and the preparation of the artwork remain the same.

Copy lighting

Even lighting

Artwork frequently needs to be lit with evenly distributed light. If it is not evenly distributed then you may get areas that are overexposed and look burned out on the screen with grey dismal fringes to the sides or edges of the caption and shadows from any raised areas. Light which is too powerful or unevenly dispersed can also cause the artwork to distort due to the amount of heat from the lights and/or its uneven distribution. There are several very simple ways to get an even light that bathes the artwork in a kindly fashion and these are known as:

- Indirect light.
- Diffused direct light.
- Balanced direct light.

Indirect lighting is got by working in the reflected light from a white wall, board or screen.

Diffused lighting is got by working inside a white tent or under an awning of light white cotton sheeting. This is also a very good way for shooting highly reflective subjects like silverware, glass and jewellery as it removes flaring specular highlights.

If you have no lights available then the free light from the sun is excellent, if unreliable in some countries. Direct sunlight is usually too strong and directional and needs to be calmed down and diffused. A bright, hazy day is ideal but you cannot rely on nature to provide this for you just when you want it. The most effective alternative is to use indirect or diffused sunlight to replicate the light cloud layer of a hazy day. (See Figure 2.)

Figure 1 Using soft reflected sunlight outdoors. Place the artwork on a simple caption stand facing a white wall, bedsheet or large piece of paper. Take care not to get shadows from yourself or the camcorder on the artwork. The camcorder will need a lens hood to shield the lens from the direct rays of the sun. Proprietory lens hoods are not quite deep enough for all circumstances. A piece of card held above the lens and just out of shot will work well. This set-up is also very suitable for portraits and people shots. It prevents them from screwing up their eyes when looking at camera and bathes them in a soft, flattering light that the video can resolve well.

Artificial lighting is more controllable but quite directional and needs to be balanced by using several sources.

While video camcorders can work in very low light levels there is often no particular advantage in using them at their lower limits. Low-powered lights can give muddy colours, and enforce the use of very wide apertures with consequent shallow depth of field, poorer lens performance, distorted colour and a noisy recording. On the other hand that could be an interesting effect, if it is appropriate to the subject.

High-powered lights cause the auto exposure to select a small aperture if shooting at the standard 'shutter' speed. Even with correct exposure they can cause glare and halation across contrasting tonal areas (the effect of light areas eating into adjacent darker ones). The heat from such lights can cause the artwork to curl, with devastating effects! As with most things a happy medium should be aimed for, which is enough light to give adequate exposure with comfortable working conditions.

Hundred-watt domestic reflector bulbs do this quite well. You will need four, two each side of the artwork arranged at 45°. Avoid any light striking the camera. Most cameras are made of black polycarbonate or similar plastic bodies that can get very hot, eventually distorting the body. Some barn doors, or similar metal shields, for the lights are a worthwhile investment. (See Figure 3.)

To ensure that the lights are giving even illumination across the artwork area, place a piece of white paper on the copyboard. The lamps should be positioned on either side of the copying area, about 500 mm away from the centre along the front to back mid-line and raised at an angle of 45° to the artwork. Examine the lit surface carefully to see if there are any dull areas caused by striations in the glass or printing on the bulb. If not, so far so good. Now hold a pencil, or similar object, vertically in the centre of the paper. The two shadows cast by the pencil should have equal density. Adjust one of the lights by moving it closer or further away from the artwork until this is so. (See Figure 5.)

Figure 2 If no white reflector is available then sunlight can be diffused by working in a tent of white material. The illustration shows a simple awning using poles but nearby posts, trees or buildings can be used just as well. It does not have to be this big, either. A small one that only contained the caption stand would be sufficient. Lastolite makes a range of circular collapsible diffusers that can be held over the caption stand.

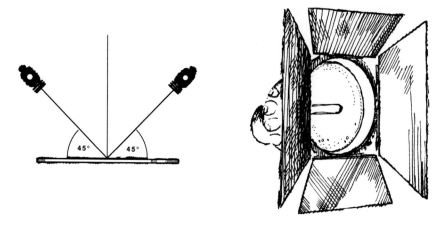

Figure 3 Barn-doors fitted to a professional tungsten halogen redhead lamp. If closed down too much they can reflect heat back into the lamp and considerably shorten bulb life. Being so close to the lamp they also get very hot and should be adjusted with a hooked rod.

If you feel like buying some useful lights there are a range of 'video lights' available which run off batteries or mains and are designed to be used on or near to the camera. This is actually the worst place to put them for general shooting as the light flattens everything and gives harsh fringing shadows. However, it isn't too bad for captions and titling. It's even better if you can bounce it off a light-coloured surface above the camera. An ordinary cheap

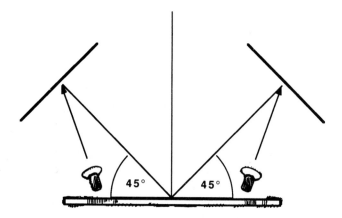

Figure 4 Domestic 100 W reflector bulbs provide enough light for most camcorders but the printing and glass irregularities on the front can throw shaded light patterns onto the artwork. The solution is to turn the bulbs 180° away from the artwork and bounce their light back from a white surface.

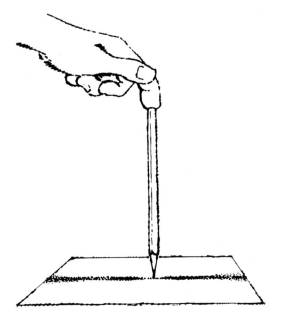

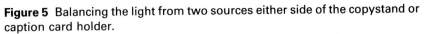

Figure 5 Balancing the light from two sources either side of the copystand or caption card holder.

white umbrella will work well, or you can buy a special photographic flash umbrella that is a little stronger and a more efficient reflector though considerably more expensive.

Directional lighting

This is mainly got by working almost in the opposite way to that needed to produce even lighting. Light originating from a single direction will throw a textured surface into dramatic relief. The quality of the light may be strong, as in a naked bulb source, which will give hard dramatic shadows, or soft, as in a diffused or indirect source, that will give correspondingly softer shadows. Angles of less than 45° are often used. There may be a problem with automatic exposure on the camcorder as it tries to rationalize between the lit and shadow areas. You will get more dramatic results if the camera's exposure is set up and locked on an evenly lit sheet which is the same colour and tone as either the graphic or its support material. When the lighting is reset to directional the shadows will be recorded with satisfactory intensity.

It is quite difficult to produce acceptable graphics directly onto a rough background material. Dry lettering cracks and distorts as you rub it down and hand drawn tends towards the difficult and irregular. If this is not the

(a)

(b)

(c)

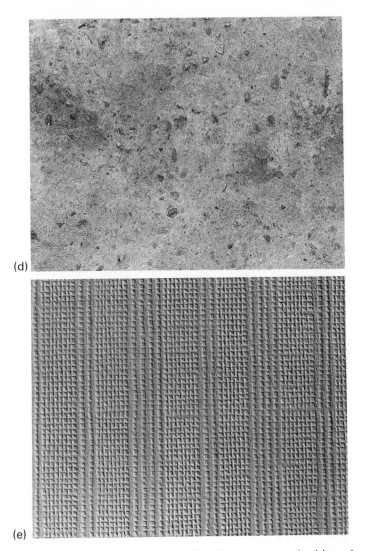

(d)

(e)

Figure 6 (a) Children's wooden alphabet letters sprayed white, placed on cork background and sidelit. (b) to (e) Samples of easily photographed textures.

effect you want this could be a good opportunity to use the camera's titling memory to replay previously recorded graphics on top of the textured background. On the other hand you could lay your dry lettering down onto acetate sheets and place these over the rough background, although it can look a bit false as it is quite evident that the flat immaculate lettering lacks any relationship with the rough undersurface.

An alternative technique, which is very convenient to use, is to make up some texture sheets by photographing rough, side-lit surfaces with colour print film. Ensure when you are photographing them that the light is coming from a direction you can replicate back in your studio. Have the film printed

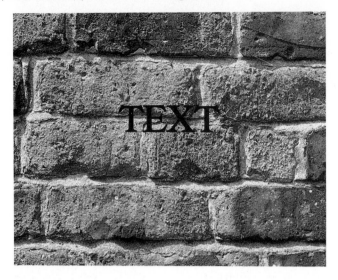

Figure 7 Instant lettering set on print of brickwork. The choice of texture, its scale as well as its relevance to the video, is crucial. Here the lettering is overpowered by the texture. On the other hand it could have been set within a brick, but then might have been too small.

to ordinary snapshot size for reference purposes. For use have selected negatives enlarged to 200 x 250 mm matt surface prints either photographically or with a colour copier. Lettering may be applied to acetate and laid on top, so saving the print for future use. You could apply it directly onto the print, which is more expensive on prints, but then you do not have to use polarizing filters to cut glare from highlights on the acetate. However, both methods still give that same strange quality of immaculate lettering on a rough surface.

The three-dimensional quality can be accentuated by using three-dimensional letters. These can be purchased from photographic shops as titling sets (though of limited typeface), from signboard manufacturers, or from children's toy shops, or you can cut them yourself with a jig saw using rub-down lettering as a guide. These are laid on the print and lit from the same direction as the light in the print. Astute viewers may notice that the shadows of the real letters do not drop into the supposed irregularities of the background, but that rarely seems to worry anyone very much. If prints are used in this way and are well looked after they will last for many years.

Exposure methods

For text or graphics that are to be reproduced in normal colour and texture, using the auto exposure and auto white balance on the camcorder will often be quite satisfactory. One great advantage of video over film is that you can see immediately on a coupled monitor how the title will look as you make adjustments to the camera. There is often a little disparity in the quality and rendering of the image between the viewfinder screen and an actual video screen so for an accurate view of effects go by the result as displayed on a video or monitor screen.

Captions and animated graphics often rely for their effectiveness on any black areas being reproduced absolutely black and featureless. Auto exposure will result in the blacks being reproduced as dark greys as the auto exposure strives to get a compromise from the high-contrast caption it has been offered. This may also show details of animation methods as well as spoiling the illusion of an infinite background to text: not a good thing.

To avoid this you should set the exposure and colour balance manually.

- Turn the auto exposure and colour balance to manual.
- Point the camera at the text or graphics.
- Connect the video output of the camera to a television set and turn the camera onto standby.
- Adjust the iris and colour balance while watching the TV until you get as near as you can to pure featureless black with the lighter text apparently floating suspended in space. Some camcorders, such as the Sony Hi8 V900, have settings on the colour balance controls that improve the rendering of monochrome subjects or bright lights against a dark background, such as firework displays. Try either of these settings until you get the desired effect. It does not matter which setting you decide is satisfactory as long as it is doing what you want. The control labels on the camera are indications, not directions. You are unlikely to harm the camera unless you are continuously burning out the scene in a fiery haze of white.

If you do not have a coupled monitor or a manual setting, turn the auto exposure and colour balance on and allow the camera to set itself on a plain sheet of the same colour and tone as the actual lettering or graphics you have made. Lock the camera at that setting before removing the sheet and replacing it with the text on the black background.

If your artwork is dark-toned on a white or coloured background then proceed as above except that in the second example you would lock the exposure on a sheet of the background material.

Polarizing filters

To shoot shiny surfaces such as glass and acetate you will need to place polarizing filters over each of the lights and one over the camera lens to reduce surface reflections. These cut out some of the light reaching the CCD chip but this will not be very noticeable unless you are working at extremely low light levels: which is another good reason for not doing so!

Take care not to work at the extremes of lens and aperture performance. However, if you have the good fortune to be working on a perfectly flat vacuum table you may be able to avoid the expense of polarizing filters. This is because a vacuum table sucks the artwork and acetates flat and the lights can be adjusted so that there is no glare; well, this is in a perfect world and it rarely happens but the table will get acetates flatter than most other methods. Correction by polarizing filters is then both easier and more effective. It is frequently on non-vacuum tables that problems arise with specular reflections from very slightly curved acetates.

The polarizing filters over the lights must initially be aligned so that both light sources will be polarized in the same direction. To do this hold the filter sheets together and while looking through them rotate one until the view through is at its clearest. Mark the tops of both sheets with a notch.

Place a filter in front of each light so that the notch is at the top in both cases. Both light sources are now polarized in the same direction. The filter on the camera is rotated gently within its mount until any reflections and glare from the shiny surface are cut out. You can see this happening in the viewfinder and on the monitor. You will probably have to experiment with the lamp positions initially, to avoid direct mirror reflections of them in the surface of the acetate. Once you have got your perfect set-up, mark it and lock everything at those settings. Occasionally the polarized light is effective enough on its own and an additional polarizing filter for the camera is unnecessary.

Polarizing sheet for the lights can be obtained from Optical Filters Ltd, Instrument Plastics Ltd, and Chequers UK Ltd (see Suppliers' List). This is fairly heat resistant but you should take care to position it away from the lights. Work to around 400 mm away from the light source. There are several different thicknesses of polarizing sheet; the very thin type needs mounting in a frame and handling with care. The thicker (HN42 Acrylic, 1.8 mm thick) is self-supporting but considerably more expensive.

Polarizing filters for your camcorder can be obtained from your local photographic dealers. Try Cokin, Hoya, or Kodak. These filters will also cut through water surfaces and alter the blue density of the sky. Travel videos and brochure photographs are nearly always shot with a polarizing filter to enhance the clarity and blueness of sea and sky and it is a useful thing to have anyway. Lovely things can be done by cutting old Polaroid™ sunglasses lenses to fit your camcorder's filter holder, or a piece of the sheet you are using for the lights. They are not optically perfect but Polaroid™ sunglasses lens flats can be obtained from Proops.

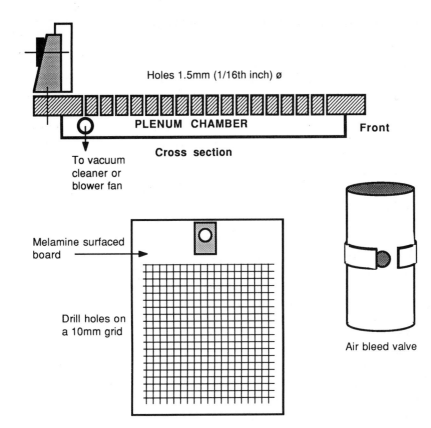

Holes 1.5mm (1/16th inch) ø

PLENUM CHAMBER   Front

Cross section

To vacuum
cleaner or
blower fan

Melamine surfaced
board

Drill holes on
a 10mm grid

Air bleed valve

Aligning polarizing sheets

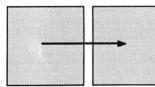

Place polarizing sheets one on
top of the other

Rotate until view
through both is at
its lightest. They are
now aligned

If the effect through
both is very dark the
sheets are not
aligned

Figure 8 A vacuum table can be made by drilling 1.5 mm (1/16 in) holes on a
10 mm grid. Construct a plenum chamber under the table. The dimensions
for this are not critical and something in the region of 20 mm deep will be
adequate. The suck is supplied by a small vacuum cleaner or blower fan
(which is much quieter). There should be an air bleed valve in the hose to
regulate the suction at the table while allowing the full supply of air to reach
the motor and keep it cool.

Copying transparencies

Slides

You may wish to use a 35 mm slide as background to titles or graphics. Perhaps the simplest way to do this is to get a 200 × 250 mm print made from it and use this on the copystand. This allows you to add acetate overlays with other graphics on them too. Sometimes this is not possible, or worth the time, trouble and expense, and a direct shot of the slide would suffice. Most camcorders with macro settings will not quite focus close enough to frame a 35 mm slide. The easiest way to do it is to use a 35 mm slide projector to project an image onto a textureless screen material. Plastic paper is ideal for this (see Lloyd Paton in Suppliers' List, also paper manufacturers or suppliers such as Wiggins Teape) and has the advantage of being translucent so the slide can be back-projected, which makes for more convenient equipment set-up and working.

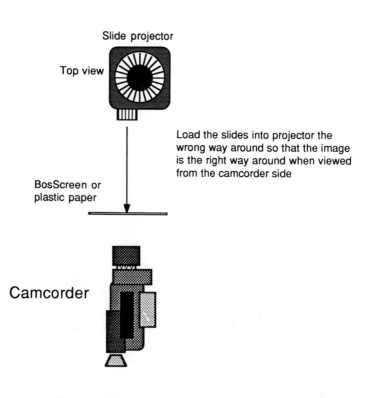

Slide projector

Top view

Load the slides into projector the wrong way around so that the image is the right way around when viewed from the camcorder side

BosScreen or plastic paper

Camcorder

Figure 9 Shooting slides by back-projection.

Alternatively the slide can be copied in the gate of the projector by shooting down the lens of the projector. This can be hazardous to the camcorder owing to the high light levels of the projector bulb. This can be controlled by placing a neutral density filter over the camcorder lens or pieces of polarizing film between the slide and the condensers. (**Not** by the bulb!)

Slide projectors are not really designed for this sort of thing and you may notice that the difference in light level between the centre of the image and its edges is accentuated on video.

Glowing lines and text

To add a feeling of luminosity and glow to artwork it is necessary to produce it in reverse and backlight it. There are several ways to go about this and your local rapid print shop or graphic arts suppliers will advise you if you do not have the equipment in-house.

Get a piece of black film or acetate with the graphic left as clear acetate: a negative, in other words. The quickest and easiest ways of getting this are by PMT or Copyproof systems or by using an Omnicrom machine. For these an original should be produced as black graphics on white paper.

The reversed material is placed on a lightbox, on the copystand. The lightbox illumination needs to be constant source, not fluorescent. Flourescent lights can give a strobing effect if the 50 cycles flicker interferes with the line scan of the camera/video. Colour gels can be added under the artwork. Place a sheet of fine-grained opalescent plastic, such as tracing acetate, immediately over the reversed artwork. Turn out all lights except the lightbox and adjust the aperture until you get the result you require. The more you intentionally overexpose, the brighter the lettering will appear, the

Figure 10 A back-projected high-contrast positive with filters added to the camcorder.

bigger the glow, but the more degraded the graphic detail and any colour you have used will become.

An alternative is to put a diffusion filter over the camcorder lens and shoot ordinary white artwork on a dark background This does lack the bite and intensity of the previous method but has a romantic soft feel of its own.

The '1400' in Figure 10 was straightforward, if somewhat involved, to produce. First a 35 mm black and white negative shot was taken of the announcement board in the airport with 1400 as large as possible. This was then copied onto Lith film to get a high-contrast positive which cut out all the unwanted detail on the board itself, and then back-projected onto a sheet of plastic paper. A soft filter and a star filter were added to the camcorder to give the softness and stars.

Photographing a video screen

The image on a video screen has a certain quality that it is very difficult to reproduce in any other graphic way. You may want to use a still from a previous programme or the interstation noise, or give a graphic a unique appearance, or you may just want a photographic record of an effect.

The results are unpredictable when shooting the screen directly with your camcorder. The colour distorts and you can get rolling bars caused by the camcorder's image scanning being out of sync with the video screen. In addition moiré patterns can appear as the line structure on the shot screen interferes with the lines on the viewing screen.

To get more control over this it is necessary to photograph the screen directly and use the resulting print or transparency as artwork. Photographing the screen is quite simple and the following technique was used to produce the screen shots used in this book.

You will need the following equipment:

- An SLR camera. This is important. A compact or any camera with a separate viewfinder will not be so easy to align with the screen. Having said that, I am sure there are many readers who can get accurate results with a compact camera and a bit of effort. Remember, the video screen has different proportions to most photographic formats and you may want to take portions of an image. An SLR does take the 'Have I got it all in?' worry out of the process.
- Manual exposure override or exposure lock is a great help in getting the exposure accurate. The built-in meters can be too successful in averaging an exposure. Some automatic cameras have a plus and minus exposure adjustment and you can use this to make exposures at either side of that indicated. At the very least there should be an exposure lock so you can set the exposure on a calibration screen. The electronics in some still cameras are sensitive to the strobing effect of the video screen

and indicate a variety of exposures from the same image. If you have one like this then you should use a hand-held meter.

- A medium telephoto lens, 100 to 135 mm for 35 mm format cameras. The medium telephoto slightly flattens the curvature of the screen and gives a more comfortable working distance from the set. A standard lens will do if you do not have a medium telephoto.
- If the camera has a motor drive or winder this will remove the risk of moving the camera during film advance. If it has not, be careful and check alignment with the screen through the viewfinder before each shot.
- Fine- to medium-grain film of about 64 to 125 ASA/ISO. If you are using a colour transparency film then it should be daylight type, even though you are shooting an image produced by artificial light. The image on the screen is low resolution to start with and if you want facsimile results there is no sense adding to this with a coarse-grain film. On the other hand it can give some lovely effects
- The tripod you use for your camcorder with full camera movements, i.e. a pan and tilt head and a rising centre column. This makes setting up very easy and accurate, but a box or a chair will do at a pinch. You are going to be using a very slow shutter speed so hand holding is out.
- Some shrouding, a large cardboard box will do, or undertake all this work in a darkened room. This not only prevents the image on the screen from being degraded by ambient light but makes your exposure more accurate and causes less light to fall on the camera and tripod. This is important because it is often possible to see a reflection of these in the video screen, especially if they have bright chrome parts. Scrupulous workers put a black board or sheet over the front of the camera/tripod with a hole cut in it for the lens to shoot through.
- Your camcorder or domestic VCR, connected to the video with the material you want to shoot on tape and loaded in it. Whichever you use it should be capable of giving a clean, noise- and judder-free freeze frame.
- An inclinometer. This can be purchased from DIY shops and is intended for checking the slope of things such as guttering. It is invaluable for setting the camera up so that its back is absolutely parallel to the screen. Left to right adjustment can be made by measurement but vertical adjustment always seems more difficult. Simply place the inclinometer against the centre of the video or monitor screen and note the reading on the inclinometer. Now place it vertically against the back of the camera and tilt the camera up or down until the inclinometer reading is the same as it was for the video/monitor screen. Now raise or lower the camera on the centre column, without tilting it, until the screen is accurately framed in the viewfinder.

Set up your equipment as in Figure 11 and focus accurately on the screen. Turn out the room lights or completely shroud camera and screen. Set the shutter speed to 1/15th second. The reason for this slow speed is that the video image is made up of 25 individual pictures transmitted each second. An additional complication is that the 625 lines that compose the picture are not laid down on the screen instantaneously or consecutively but are scanned down the screen from the top left-hand corner, all the odd-numbered lines first in a 50th of a second, then all the even ones between in the next 50th. Because of the speed at which this happens, the persistence of our vision and the fluorescence of the screen we do not notice this happening. The camera, however, would freeze this process with a shutter speed higher than a 15th, resulting in bars or diagonal stripes across the screen or partly completed pictures.

This is why the video recorder with clean freeze frame is used. At these slow shutter speeds any live action would be blurred so the recorder is used to freeze the action for you. Start the video and freeze on the frame you want to record.

For average scenes allow the camera meter to set/suggest the aperture with the shutter speed set at 1/15th or 1/8th of a second. Bracket this exposure by shooting duplicate shots with the aperture set half a stop higher and half a stop lower than that indicated as correct. Do not make exposure adjustments by altering the shutter speed. Remember, you need the slow speed to ensure that the complete video picture build up is recorded.

Coloured text or thin line drawings on a black or very dark background, such as light titles or the text on some computer screens, pose a different problem. The camera meter is affected by the large area of black and will suggest or set an aperture that is too large, resulting in overexposed text and a background that lacks richness. To record such images accurately, flood the screen with a solid version of the colour used in the text or drawing and allow the camera to meter this. Alternatively use the same exposure as that indicated for a normal average image. Set the indicated aperture or if you are using an automatic camera lock it at that aperture.

When taking a print film to be processed by your high street lab tell them that it contains video screen shots and that blacks should be really black. This is especially important for text or thin line drawings on black. You may have done a good job in photographing them accurately but the printing machine also has an automatic exposure system that can be influenced by the large area of black and will need some compensation by the operator to give a correctly exposed print.

A word about copyright. Assume the content of all broadcast material is copyright, as will be screen images from well-known computer software. The safest course of action is only to photograph what you have generated.

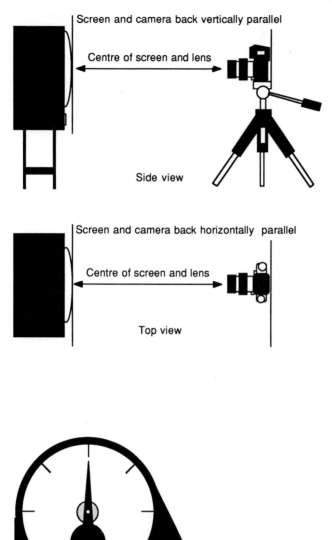

Screen and camera back vertically parallel

Centre of screen and lens

Side view

Screen and camera back horizontally parallel

Centre of screen and lens

Top view

Inclinometer

Photographing a video screen

Figure 11 The equipment set-up for photographing a video screen.

A basic caption stand

A caption stand is an extremely useful, yet simple piece of equipment. Having made one and used one you wonder how you managed so long without it.

Because stability is important the construction must be sound and the materials robust.

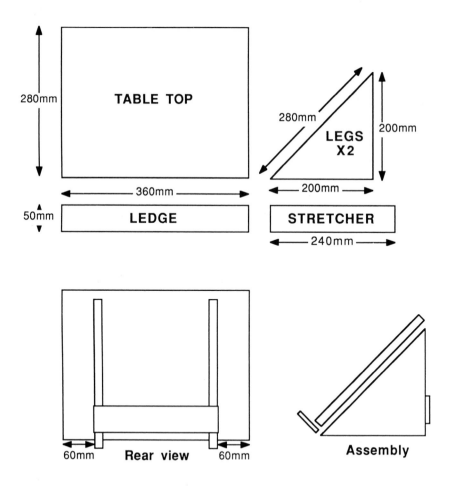

Figure 12 Making a simple caption stand.

Copystand construction

A copystand is a simple item to make and should be regarded as essential for videoing artwork or even animations. Some care is needed in the construction to ensure that the whole thing is robust and wobble free. If you are going to have it made for employees, or others, to use then make it very strong. If in doubt err on the side of over-engineering!

One of the most flexible and robust materials to use for the construction is slotted angle such as 'Dexion' or 'Handy Angle'. Choose the heaviest gauge for stability. The column is made up from two strips bolted together to form a U. Two longer pieces at the bottom support the copyboard while smaller pieces bolted to the sides form the camcorder bracket. This bracket does not have to be adjustable once you have found your most convenient working distance.

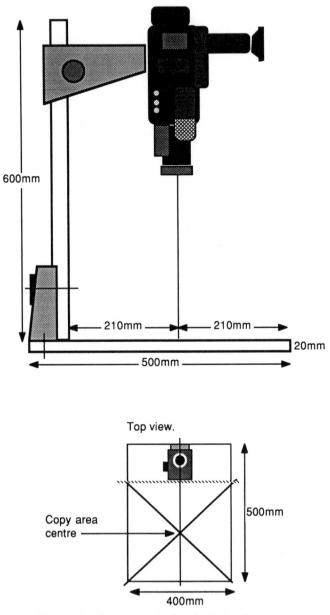

600mm

210mm 210mm

20mm

500mm

Top view.

Copy area
centre

500mm

400mm

Ensure that the camcorder is adjusted on its mount so
that the lens centre coincides with the copy area centre

Figure 13 The dimensions given are for guidance only. The principles to be observed are:

● Make the rostrum to fit your video camcorder. Commerical copystands are made to suit all models and formats of camera, so are often unnecessarily huge. Place yourself by the table or bench on which you will use the finished copystand. Measure the distance from your eye level to the table surface. We shall call this distance 'eye to table'. Check that your camcorder can focus at this distance; most will do so. If it cannot then consider making a horizontal copystand or work with a lower table height.

● The baseboard material needs to be flat, rigid and unlikely to warp. 15 mm blockboard of 10-ply is very suitable. Marine ply is even better because the ply glue is waterproof.

● Fix your camcorder onto a tripod. Tape a piece of white paper onto a wall. Move the tripod until the camera is 'eye to table' distance away from the paper. While looking through the viewfinder ask someone to mark the corners of the viewfinder frame on the paper. This will give you the rectangle the camera 'sees' at that distance. Cut your material for your baseboard an extra 100 mm all around.

● The rear column must be rigidly fixed to the baseboard and at a perfect right angle. A 30 mm diameter tube works well and should be considered as the minimum diameter for stability.

● The carriage to hold the camera needs to be adjustable over about 150 mm. General purpose commercial copystands often have a carriage with two sliding adjustments, one front and rear of 150 mm, the other up and down on a 1 m column. This is to accommodate different makes of camera and lens combinations and different sizes of artwork. As you are making a stand for a particular camera and a set size of artwork this degree of adjustment is unnecessary. Ensure that the carriage is large enough for the centre of the camera lens to line up with a point midway between the column and the front of the baseboard. Two lights of equal power should be mounted so that:

● The lamps are above the camcorder lens height.

● They are equally spaced from the centre of the baseboard.

● They are each inclined at an angle of 45° to the centre of the baseboard.

See Copy lighting, pp. 3–7.

2 Text and Layout

Colour

Videocameras have certain idiosyncrasies associated with their rendering of colours. These are to do with the design and limitations of the pickup device (CCD or Tube) and the subsequent electronics. Obviously the more you pay the better the performance but all camcorders display a certain reluctance to resolve saturated reds and deep blues accurately. On the other hand greens, lighter blues and yellows are all resolved well; oddly, some camcorders have difficulty with green/blue mixtures such as turquoise, jade and eau-de-nil and tend to replay them as light blue. To test the capabilities of your camcorder make a test shot of a variety of colours. The easiest way to do this is to use a paint manufacturer's colour card. Artists' colours have the greatest range, decorating paints tend to be pastels and of limited range. It's a good idea to take one of these with you when contemplating buying a camcorder and do a test shot in the shop. You will be quite surprised at some of the replies and observations you will get from sales assistants when you ask them about any perceived colour inaccuracy.

A single CCD chip is considerably better than a single tube of equivalent standard but the limited bandwidth assigned to deep blue and red colours still causes occasional problems. What tends to happen is that the camcorder records red and deep blue a little inaccurately and displays difficulty in resolving different hues and shades of red and deep blue. Also chroma noise, generated by the system, is more easily seen in these colours. This gives a speckling or flickering effect within the colour. Another effect often seen most obviously in reds is chroma shift, or smear, where the red elements of the picture are slightly displaced from their proper physical position, often slightly below and to the left or right. This is due to delay within the electronics in getting that component of the signal recorded onto the tape and is exacerbated by multiple generations and worn tape heads. S-VHS and Hi8 formats have addressed this problem quite well with improved electronics, separation of the composite signal through S terminals when connecting camcorders to other tape machines, and the use of metal tape. The provision of an edit switch also improves quality when transferring onto other tapes by giving the signal a boost to compensate for that lost in the process. Despite all these enhancements red smear and chroma noise still occurs.

To remedy this, avoid using deep blues or reds if possible. Certainly avoid important detail in hues and tones of red or blue within the same shot as they will not be rendered with sufficient distinctiveness. If you have to use a red then ensure that the artwork is well lit so that there is plenty of signal from the CCD. In this way whatever chroma noise is present becomes less evident.

The effect of chroma shift, or smearing, may be reduced in text and graphics that contain a red fill by surrounding them with a black outline. How thick an outline you need will be determined by your particular equipment, so you will need to experiment, but the results are quite effective.

Colour and mood

The considered use of colour in titles and graphics is essential. The appropriate choice of colour can establish a mood or attitude or simply accentuate details that have greater importance. It is quite difficult to lay down 'rules' for the use of colour because factors such as fashion, cultural perceptions and personal choice affect the viewer's response. However, there are some broad guidelines that are generally regarded as workable:

- Work to a limited colour scheme and stick to this for all graphics to maintain unity and harmony throughout the video. A way to determine a series of colours that will harmonize together is to consider the colour circle.

Figure 14 depicts the colour circle in glorious monochrome. Colours which lie beside each other on the circle will harmonize well with each other; colours harmonize gradually less well the further apart they are chosen. Colours which lie opposite each other are contrasting colours. The primary colours are red, yellow and blue, so called because they cannot be mixed from any other colour combination. The secondary colours are orange (red and yellow), green (blue and yellow) and purple (red and blue).

- Pure colours of red, orange and yellow are preferred by young children with connotations of danger, fire, funfairs, children's toys and important objects like post boxes, buses and eye-catching signs. Red is the colour least well resolved by video.
- As people mature, their preference tends to shift towards blues and greens and many find that these have a calming and restful effect. Waiting rooms and operating theatres are often decorated in greens for this reason.
- The continued use of pure colours would be visually very restless and aggressive and it is in their mixtures, tints and shades where subtlety and huge variety can be employed. Pastel colours (any colour with the addition of white) are the sort many of us use to decorate our homes. It is quite difficult in the UK to buy decorator's paint in strong colours.

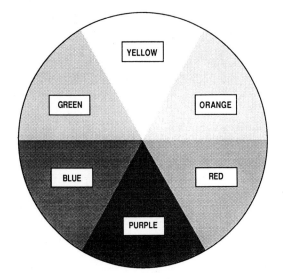

Figure 14 This is the subtractive colour system used when dealing with reflected light. Transmitted light uses the additive colour system that has primaries of red, green and blue; hence the RGB input on the backs of monitors, because the television system uses the additive system. However, we are dealing with reflected light from the graphics so will use the subtractive system illustrated here. The primary colours are more accurately named magenta (red), cyan (blue) and process yellow (yellow).

Pastel colours tend to recede from the viewer. This may be because we associate diluted colour with objects at a great distance. Strong colours appear to advance, although strong blues appear to recede because the combination of the physical structure of the eye and the wavelength of the colour makes it a difficult colour to focus. Hence were you to create a title with a strong blue text or diagram on a background of a different colour with a similar tone you would find it uncomfortable to interpret.

- The predominant colour of the actual video programme can be reflected in the graphics to maintain unity and complement the visual style. The landscape of Crete in August is predominantly brown. Underwater is blue/green. Spring in the UK is greens or yellows. Captions in an industrial video might use the colours of the material being worked.
- Thought must also be given to the cultural perceptions of the audience regarding their use of colour in everyday life and the connotations they give it. For many Chinese white is the colour of sadness and mourning while red is happiness, good luck, wealth and their colour for marriage. The American Indians regard red as a colour of misfortune. Hindus regard yellow as a colour for marriage and happiness, while for Western audiences it can symbolize jealousy and treason or have links with

warning markings such as yellow and black stripes. In certain Arab cultures green is seen as a colour to ward off evil spirits and more generally it is the sacred colour of Islam. Certainly it also has connotations of earth, life and environmental concern. Purple has associations with regality, possibly because it was a difficult, and hence expensive, colour to produce as a dye.

Contrast

An important factor in aiding legibility is the contrast ratio between the image/text and the background. Were this book to be printed in black on dark grey paper (a low contrast ratio) you would find it quite difficult to read, irrespective of the typestyle and layout used. Generally a high contrast ratio produces the most legible results but avoid the extremes, like bright glaring backgrounds that can make legibility difficult.

Contrast can be manipulated by:

- The selection of widely separated tones on the scale from black to white. A colour with any amount of white added to it is a tint; one with any amount of black added is a shade. This book uses the tonal scale extremes, black print on white paper, but often for video this is too glaring as the light from a white screen is greater than that from white paper. Also it is not good practice to use pure white in front of the camcorder. Although chip cameras are far more tolerant than the older designs, white still tends to flare and be resolved as a featureless blob. It is much safer to use a pale colour.
- The selection of opposite colours from the colour circle. This can make for maximum arresting quality and garishness but is likely to be rather uncomfortable to view.
- The use of different graphic patterns, for example smooth lettering on a finely patterned background of the same colour and tone.

Figure 15 Plain text on patterned background.

- The use of different physical textures, for example drawing in wet sand.

Grids

In all captions and graphics thought must be given at the outset to the positioning of information in similar positions from graphic to graphic. This enables the audience to recognize a consistent style and be prepared for information in a certain place. Without a consistent style, or grammar, the audience has to reinterpret each graphic, which makes the conveying of information less efficient.

The usual way to define a layout is to use a grid. This can be of any shape or proportion suitable to the screen and content but once chosen every graphic or title in that video should conform to it.

Proportions and useful working sizes

This is essential information where artwork or captions are being prepared for video, film etc. so that you can produce graphics that will fit the format of the medium. It also enables you to determine a size that is convenient for you to work on while being easily recorded by your equipment.

Video and computer monitor screens, 35 mm and 16 mm cine film have proportions of 4:3. Thus a piece of artwork must measure 4 units wide by 3 units high to match the video format precisely.

There are standard cut paper sizes that are very close to this already. Most useful is the 254 × 203 mm (10 × 8 in) photographic paper. However, usually it is not so important to have the paper or board correct provided that the actual graphic has the right proportions and there is plenty of safety margin between it and the edges.

All 'A' paper sizes have the same proportion, 2.84:2, which is very close to the 35 mm still frame proportion of 3:2. This makes it useful as a guide for designing 35 mm slide graphics but too wide for video. A4 used landscape (297 mm wide × 210 mm high) is a convenient size to use on a copy stand

Figure 16 Grids. The use of a grid does not limit your interpretation within that grid to something identical throughout the video. The top illustration shows a simple grid; the subsequent illustrations show text and picture areas manipulated within it. The audience would quickly recognize that illustrations always appeared on the right-hand side and text on the left. Though of differing proportions the text and illustrations obey the grid in proportion. In this example their areas are always multiples of the horizontal lines and their width is constant to the margins. You may be more ambitious and use extra vertical margins but this might cut up the text into very narrow columns that would require a smaller typeface that would be less well resolved on the screen. Keep things simple!

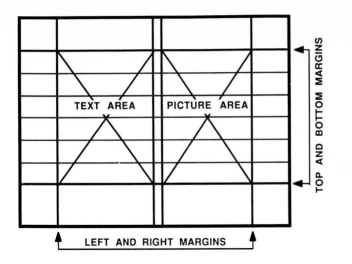

TEXT AREA   PICTURE AREA

TOP AND BOTTOM MARGINS

LEFT AND RIGHT MARGINS

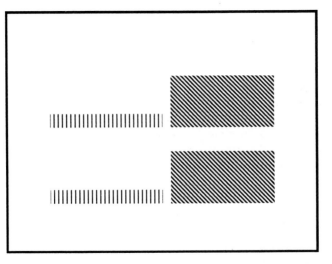

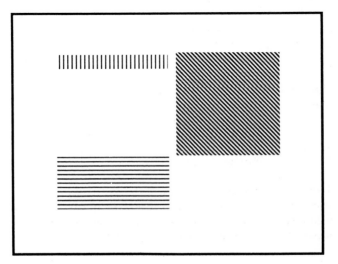

but you should work on a centred rectangle within it of 180 × 135 mm. This will give the 4:3 video proportion and a useful margin for handling and safety. All camcorders can shoot this size and while most can go a good deal smaller with macro settings there is often no great advantage in working at the fiddly end of things.

It speeds up work enormously if you make a template of a piece of A4 robust card with a 180 × 135 mm window cut in the centre. Place it on top of any A4 sheet and mark the corners of the window to give yourself a guide. This also ensures that all graphics will be in the same place on each successive card and so there will be less lining up to do by the cameraperson.

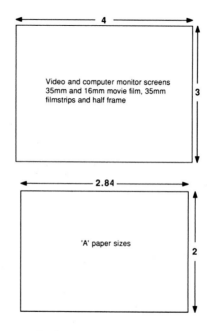

Figure 17 Basic proportions for video artwork.

Typefaces

Suitable styles for video

Video is a low-definition medium composed at present of 625 lines. Because of this image structure certain typefaces resolve more legibly than others. The clearest styles are those that are bold and without fine serifs. The worst are those with flowery curlicues and fine pointed serifs.

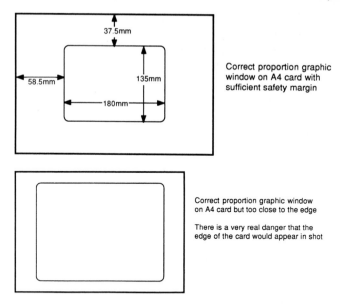

Correct proportion graphic window on A4 card with sufficient safety margin

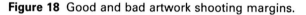

Correct proportion graphic window on A4 card but too close to the edge

There is a very real danger that the edge of the card would appear in shot

Figure 18 Good and bad artwork shooting margins.

Matching typestyle to programme

This is an enormous subject for which it is almost impossible to set rules. In every video the style of the typeface used should compliment, or intentionally contrast, the subject or learning outcome of the video. The continual use of some typestyles for certain subject matters has become clichéd, such as Playbill or Calliope for any music hall act or Wild West epic.

Times Roman tends to be used for anything with a remotely classical content, often in a chisel face version for extra classicism! The typeface in Figure 21 is a derivative of Times and has been given a chisel effect.

To make matters more complicated, typography (the design and use of typefaces) is fraught with fashionable trends. The underlying intention is to use a typeface and layout that combines the virtues of relevance to your audience and the video content, aesthetic appeal and legibility. I advise you to do some simple research. Consider your target audience. What magazines or newspapers are targeted towards them? Look at them, analyse how they are laid out, the type they use etc. Consider the content of the video. Would that sort of layout and typestyle be appropriate? What would the target audience consider appropriate? Very often the content or location of the video will suggest a typestyle which reflects or reinforces typestyles frequently seen in the programme. These can be used as titling.

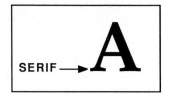

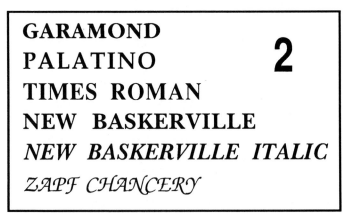

Figure 19 The selection of typestyles in group 1 would resolve well on video as they share a certain chunky unfussiness; those in group 2 less so, being more delicate. Much also depends upon the size of the type as displayed on screen, its colour, contrast etc. A full-screen letter from Zapf Chancery would be clear, one about 4 mm high much less so! Aim for a minimum screen letter height of 15 mm that gives legibility at a comfortable viewing distance for the audience.

Figure 20 Playbill and Calliope typefaces.

Figure 21 Trump-gravur typeface.

There are a few pitfalls that can be recognized in advance:

- The use of a cartoon or informal style of lettering for a very formal or serious content.
- The use of a typeface that has strong associations with other inappropriate matter, such as income tax forms.
- The use of a layout that is so stylized that few people can interpret it.
- The use of capital letters (which look as if the text is shouting) where upper and lower case would have been more approachable.

- The use of entirely lower case that looks stylish but is upsetting to read as there are few visual rhythms to help recognize the words.
- The use of every typeface that can be found.

Favourite clichés:

- The use of Olde Englyshe scripts for anything to do with anything Olde Englyshe.
- The use of Gothic script for anything ecclesiastical or German; but probably essential for anything with a heavy metal rock music content!
- The use of computer style typefaces for anything to do with new technology or space travel.
- Any typeface that has been bent and distorted along a wavy line for anything to do with water.
- Any typeface that looks like shiny metal and has star point highlights on it for any purpose at all.
- Letters which look as if they have been carved out of a gigantic cliff for anything to do with a serious epic.

Of course you can deliberately use these if you wish to make a statement about the cliché or purposefully set the audience up to expect something, or just send up the whole genre.

Lettering and typesetting methods

The easiest way to set lettering is to use an Apple Macintosh coupled to a laserprinter. If you do not have these then many high street quick print shops will set text for you.

Failing this the next best is to use Letraset, Mecanorma, Blick or similar rub-down instant lettering. These can be purchased in quite small sheets. Rubbing the letters down is rather laborious, especially if misspelling occurs, but the protagonists say that the letterforms in instant lettering are far more accurate than laserprinted letters. The typefaces illustrated are from the excellent Mecanorma range.

Rule very faint guide lines using a B or 2B sharp pencil and line your text up on this. Space the individual letters apart optically.

You are trying to get a similar area of space within and between the letters, not a set space between letter extremities. This means some letters like A and V will have to be spaced closer together than N and I. Look closely at the cover of this book and you will see that the letters are not spaced equidistant

Figure 22 A selection of five typefaces whose use has become overly associated with certain subjects. See how many associations you can make.

Magnetic

ABCDEFGH
IJKLMNOP
QRSTUVW!
XYZ12345
67890?!&
%, ." "";:-$

Jim crow

ABCDEFG
HIJKLMNO
PQRSTUW
VXYZ-1234

Television

ABCDEFG
HIJKLMN!
OPQRST?
UVWXYZ:1
2345678!

Art deco

ABCDEFGH
IJKLMNOP?
QRSTUVXY
WZÆŒÇ12
3456789&
()%£$|(/△‹›

Update

ABCDEFGH:
IJKLMNOP;
QRSTUVW!
XYZÆŒÇØ
234567890

POOR SPACING

BETTER SPACING

F • A • S • H • I • O • N

Figure 23 Poor and effective letter spacing. Just as we think we know where we are, along comes something which deliberately breaks the conventions for effect. This is a reworking of an earlier fashion in the 1920s.

apart. When each letter has been rubbed down, burnish it thoroughly by rubbing it with the back of your fingernail through the backing sheet.

Working on a separate piece of paper, cut out the set words on a strip and paste them down with cow gum in position on a clean sheet, working to your grid. Remove the pencil lines with a soft plastic eraser. Photocopy this if the edges of the cut pieces show up on screen.

There are instant lettering machines like Kroy that will output a self-adhesive tape of set text but these are very expensive.

3 Illustration

Illustration for video

The term illustration is used here to denote any type of pictorial original that may be hand drawn, photographed, collaged etc. but excludes type and lettering. However, many constraints mentioned for typography apply for illustrations.

The video medium imposes some limitations upon the designer. While technology advances at impressive speed with regard to the size and capabilities of the hardware, certain facts remain and need to be considered.

- Video is a low-definition medium. Fine detail will not be satisfactorily resolved. Thin lines, like swirly script typefaces, will be lost. Herringbone patterns or diagonal shading lines can interfere optically with the 625-line composition of the screen and cause moiré interference patterns.

You can easily check to see whether or not your illustration will be satisfactorily resolved on screen by giving it a quick test shoot on the camera. Sometimes this is not possible and anyway a quicker and easier way is to measure the width of your illustration, multiply it by 12 and stand that distance away from it. What you can see easily will reproduce well on screen and be legible from normal viewing distances.

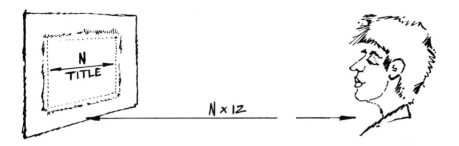

Figure 24 Testing for screen legibility.

- Use red with care; it is the most difficult colour for the system to resolve satisfactorily, especially strong, rich reds. These tend to degrade, and become muddy and are prone to smearing and break-up on screen.

- Sizes: a convenient working size for graphics is a centred rectangle of 180 × 135 mm on an A4 card.
- Take care to keep the surface of your illustration clean. Smudgy marks caused by cheap pencil erasers will show up, as will pencil guide-lines. The latter are especially prone to flaring and shining when used on black card or paper.
- Exceed your shooting area boundaries. Camcorder viewfinders are not renowned for their pinpoint accuracy and edges may show on screen.

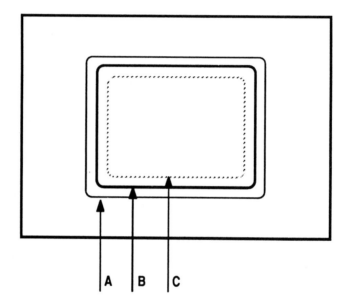

Figure 25 Rectangle B is the actual shooting area; however, if the graphic stopped right at the edge of this rectangle it is very likely that this break between graphic and card would be seen in shot. Also, a graphic that is so precisely drawn to its shooting area is difficult and time consuming to line up on camera. It is much better to draw the graphic so that it continues over the actual shooting area by about 20 mm all around (rectangle A). Ensure that important material remains within the shooting area. Many television sets are badly adjusted with reference to the actual picture area displayed on screen and even correctly adjusted ones lose a bit of picture around the curved sides of the tube. To compensate for this, work to a rectangle of about 10 mm smaller all around than the main shooting area and consider this to be the actual edge of the screen as seen by the audience (rectangle C). Remember to always line up the camera on the shooting area, rectangle B.

- CCD camcorders will cope with white surfaces reasonably well. However they still seem to reproduce with a burned-out look if not carefully lit. It is advisable, therefore, to avoid large areas of white. If you must have a pale surface use pale blue or pale yellow. These will

Illustration 39

tend to look white anyway without the flaring problems and reduce the contrast ratio, so leading to more satisfactory reproduction of the whole caption or illustration.

Graphics equipment and materials

Basic equipment

Good tools designed for the job make life much easier, so do always try to buy the best available.

Brushes

You will probably only need a few brushes to start with. Resist the temptation to economize on quality. Cheap brushes have very little spring, that is the hair stays bent after having applied colour to the paper, or worse, splays out. They also wear out very quickly and hairs can be left behind on the artwork.

It really is more cost effective to buy sable hair brushes. They keep their points, even when laden with colour, have excellent spring and with reasonable care and attention will last for years. Winsor & Newton designer's sable series 3a, sizes 2 (small) and 5 (average) with a round point will do to start. A flat sable, around 10 mm wide, is very useful for small washes and brushmark effects.

Figure 26 Different types of brushes. This selection would provide a basic set. Top to bottom: No.5 Artist's Sable with round point, Sable 10 mm flat, a No.2 Sable round point and a 20 mm decorator's brush.

School-type hog hair or synthetic bristle brushes are useful for applying thick colour over broad areas.

A 25-mm-wide brush is necessary for applying washes or thicker colour evenly over large areas. A decorator's brush will do quite well although cheap ones rapidly shed their bristles.

Burnisher

This is a small flat-ended instrument for rubbing down dry transfer lettering, which gives a better result than rubbing the lettering down with a ballpoint pen which presses into the paper or card and distorts the lettering, or even cracks it. They are available in artists' and graphic supplies shops but if you are unable to obtain one then the smooth end of a paint brush or a knitting needle will do just as well.

Figure 27 Two types of instant lettering burnisher. Top: Flat plastic. Bottom: Alloy with round handle and specially shaped 'blade'.

Cutting boards

You will find yourself cutting things out or trimming card to size a lot of the time. It is not a good idea to use a drawing board for this as the knife grooves rapidly destroy the drawing board's smooth surface, and it doesn't do the knife blade a lot of good either!

You need a soft but firm board. Sundeala compressed board used for notice boards and often stocked by timber merchants in 8 × 4 sheets is very good, especially if you can get an offcut. Failing this a robust card or pulp board will do. The idea is to provide a surface the knife or scalpel can bite into but which is not so hard that it blunts the blade. Hardboard is not satisfactory.

Take care that the old knife tracks do not divert your blade away from the new cut line you are trying to follow.

There are some special cutting boards made that overcome this problem. They have a self-healing plastic layer laminated onto a firm acrylic base. In addition there is an accurate grid printed on them to help line up paper and cut. However, they are quite expensive and should only be used with scalpels, certainly not heavier knives that can penetrate into the acrylic base and prevent the self-healing plastic healing smoothly.

Straight Edge

A straight edge is used to check for straightness, line things up etc. but more usefully to cut along with a knife or scalpel.

Illustration 41

Figure 28 Stainless steel 500 mm-long straight edge.

Invest in a metal straight edge. The mild steel ones are reasonably priced and quite serviceable if you keep them clean and dry; otherwise they rust and mark your work. Many years ago when I was a student I bought a stainless steel one, which seemed to use an awful lot of grant at the time, but I never regretted buying it. I still have it now, 30 years later, as clean, bright and straight as it was when new.

Drawing board

This can be any smooth piece of wood about 12 mm thick. Nine ply is very suitable as it resists warping. The board should not flex and must have accurate, straight edges parallel to each other with right angle corners so that a T-square will give parallel lines down the board.

Professional wooden drawing boards are cramped and battened to prevent distortion and have an aluminium or hard plastic edging let into the side to guide a T-square.

It is possible to buy plastic drawing boards by Rötring and Staedtler that have built-in paper clips, sliding T-square and various other refinements. Usual sizes are A4 and A3.

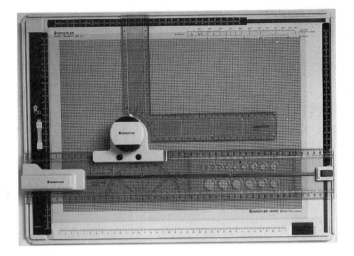

Figure 29 Plastic drawing/drafting board with parallel motion and set square. Photo courtesy of Staedtler Mars.

Drawing instruments

The most useful are:

- T-square. Used with an accurate drawing board this will enable you to line up your sheets of paper or card on the drawing board then get accurate parallel lines vertically and horizontally.

Figure 30 T-square.

- Adjustable set square. Used on the T-square it saves having to turn the T-square around to get vertical lines. In addition it will give accurate angles. Try a Faber-Castell 59–42.

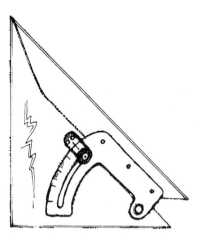

Figure 31 Adjustable set square. The sloping edge will swing out up to 90°.

- Ruler: clear plastic, robust and with parallel lines engraved along the whole length. Both inch and metric scales are useful; length around 500 mm or 18″. (See also Rolling ruler, p. 48.)

Illustration 43

Compass pen and pencil

It is possible to buy these items singly but, again, go for quality. Get a spring type with an interchangeable lead and pen unit. The bow pen units always seem to flood or run out of ink at the critical moment. A better solution is to use a compass made for one of the technical drawing pens like Rötring. This gives a controlled line of even width whatever the angle of the compass.

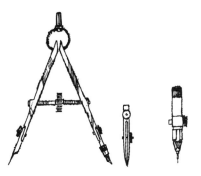

Figure 32 Left to right: spring bow compass fitted with chisel point lead; bow pen accessory; and Rötring pen accessory. The latter is to be preferred to the bow pen as it is less likely to flood and the line widths are absolute.

Erasers

Rubber erasers have been superseded by soft plastic ones that do not smear. Many different makes are available but avoid really cheap ones. AV and ink erasers tear the surface of paper; an AV eraser is designed to remove overhead projector pen from acetate.

Guillotines

Technically guillotine refers to the swing blade type of cutter, from the small type for light card up to guillotines that will cut a stack of paper or card 400 mm thick.

A guillotine is probably beyond the means of the home video enthusiast but is one of those things that are really indispensable if you are going to be doing a lot of card and paper cutting.

The safest type to buy are those with a sharp wheel, such as Rotatrim. Called rotary trimmers, these will cut anything from tissue to 3 mm-thick board. These are also safer than blade guillotine.

A general note regarding both guillotines and trimmers: the offcut is often given rippled edges by the action of the blade or cutting wheel. So, the piece

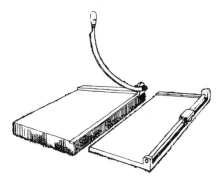

Figure 33 Left to right: traditional blade guillotine without guard; rather dangerous but cuts card well; a Rotary trimmer, much safer and cuts thin paper very well.

that you want to use must be the piece that is left on the guillotine or trimmer, not the offcut.

Knives

Two sorts of knives are all you will need: a Stanley knife for card and a scalpel for light card, papers and foam board. The Stanley knife with a retractable blade ensures the blade is kept in good condition. It is also marginally safer.

Figure 34 A selection of knives. Top to bottom: Stanley craft knife, very robust for card to carpets. Swann Morten scalpels, ideal for fine cutting of paper, prints etc., The middle one, No. 3 handle with a 10a blade, could be considered as general purpose. I find the bottom one, a No. 5 handle with a 10a blade, is more comfortable to hold and turns in the hand more easily as intricate outlines are followed.

A Swann Morten No. 3 handle with a 10a blade makes a very good general purpose tool. Some people prefer the lighter, longer and more delicate No. 5 handle, which also takes the 10a blade.

In both cases always use a very sharp blade. A dull blade tears the material and is more likely to slip out of the cut as you apply pressure. The blades can be resharpened on an oilstone. For safety and to retain its sharpness push the blade into an old bottle cork when not in use.

Illustration 45

Pencils

For most of the work in this book you will need only one pencil, a B or 2B. The reason for using a fairly soft lead is that you do not have to press so hard to get a line, so there is less likely to be a groove in the card or paper that can show up.

Choose a good pencil from a renowned manufacturer such as Cumberland, Staedtler, or Faber-Castell. These should have bonded leads, which will be less likely to crack if accidentally dropped.

Pens

Fibre-tipped pens are adequate for most of the drawing you will need. One with a line thickness of 0.5 mm should be the thinnest. Very thin lines will break up on screen. Use permanent ink as this is water resistant and a wash can be applied to parts of the drawing later if required without dissolving the ink again.

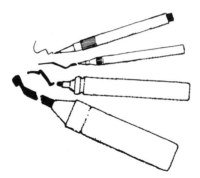

Figure 35 Fibre- and felt-tipped pens. Choose a permanent water-resistant ink and check before purchase that the ink does not fur out from the marked line.This is caused as much by the type of paper as a certain type of volatile spirit-based ink. Test it on a sample of your card or paper to be sure. Top to bottom: Fibre-tipped pen, available in 0.01 to 0.05 mm widths and a variety of inks; the 0.3 and 0.5 size are probably the most useful for video graphics. Chisel fibre-tip 2 mm wide. Bullet fibre point marker typically 4 mm wide. Felt-tip marker typically 5 mm wide. Very useful for large lettering and large area coverage.

Rolling ruler

This is a ruler with a roller built into it, rather like a navigator's parallel ruler. It is very useful for ruling parallel lines and drawing circles.

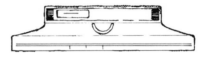

Figure 36 Rolling ruler.

Basic materials

Adhesives

Avoid any form of water-based adhesive. The water soaks into the paper or card base, causing it to expand. As it dries the paper shrinks back almost, but not quite, to its original size, causing characteristic bowing and cockling of the artwork. It can also rewet any water-soluble paint or ink, causing bleeding and smearing.

The most useful paper adhesive is cow gum. This is a rubber-based adhesive with a petroleum solvent base, which does not rewet the artwork. Cow gum can be used wet: coat the underside of the artwork with gum and gently slip the piece to be stuck into its final position. Use a proper spreader for this, as it will apply a good smooth layer.

Alternatively it can be used dry as a contact adhesive. Coat both the underside of the artwork and a little over the area it will occupy on the support. Do not worry about the extra showing around the edges as it can easily be removed later.

Allow both layers of gum to dry completely (this takes about 10 minutes), then bring both pieces together. You have to be very accurate with your positioning because you don't get a second chance!

Clean around the edges with a lump of dry cow gum rubber, made by rolling up the dried bits of gum from around the rim of the tin and using it like an eraser.

Cow gum vapour is inflammable. Do not work near naked lights. The evaporating petrol vapours can cause some photocopy inks to detach themselves from the paper and stick to the underside of the sheet on top. To avoid this lay the glued sheets out separately until all the vapour has evaporated. This usually only takes about 10 to 15 minutes.

For card and animation constructions I would recommend Uhu all-purpose clear adhesive, which is very strong and quick to dry, or a hot glue gun. For those odd bondings, such as plastic snap fasteners into recessed holes, elastic bands to card etc., super glue works very well. These are applied conventionally as wet or hot glue with the objects held in place until it dries or cools.

Spray adhesives are effective, but wasteful and can be inhaled with unpleasant effects. Ideally you should use a cardboard spray booth with these as the stuff gets everywhere.

Illustration 47

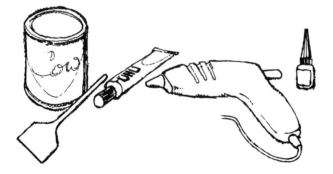

Figure 37 A collection of adhesives. Left to right: cow gum and spreader; UHU extra clear adhesive; hot glue gun and super glue.

Correcting fluid

Tipp-Ex, Liquid Paper or similar typewriter correcting fluid is invaluable for correcting small mistakes or blemishes, or making alterations to artwork. It might be seen on camera as it is often just that bit brighter than the paper and raised a little too. If this is a problem make a photocopy of the artwork and use that. Correcting fluid will not show up on the photocopy.

Inks

For most cases the black ink in the fibre-tipped pens mentioned earlier will suffice for black line drawing. If you need to cover larger areas or use a brush for drawing then you will need a bottle of Indian ink or waterproof black drawing ink. Very intense transparent coloured inks can also be obtained from artists' materials shops and these reproduce well on screen. Winsor and Newton drawing inks are supplied in small 35-ml bottles. As they are waterproof when dry, layers of other colours can be applied over each other, giving secondary mixing effects. Brushes and pens must be cleaned while wet or they will set solid when dry due to the shellac in the ink. If this happens to you, try soaking them in domestic bleach or paint stripper.

Paint

Designer's gouache is a very intense, rich, opaque, water-based paint with a wide selection of colours and is quite suitable for most applications.

For painting colour onto acetate sheets (like animators) use Pelikan Plaka or a similar casein-based paint that will lie on the acetate without running into droplets. The trick is to apply the paint to the underside of the sheet and video it from the top. This gives the colour a certain intensity and removes any surface texture effects that might otherwise be seen. It is possible to buy actetate with a very thin gelatine layer applied to it that will take any paint, but this is not always readily available. See Filmsales in the Suppliers' List.

There is also a range of designer's liquid acrylic colours in 30-ml dropper bottles by Winsor and Newton that appear to act rather like a cross between coloured inks and gouache. They are very intense and have a wide range of uses.

Paper and board

There are many paper and board suppliers in the UK, and even more worldwide. There are, however, certain basic requirements for video graphics.

- All materials must be matt surfaced, whatever the colour. You might be tempted to think that all drawing and mounting papers are more or less matt surfaced. This is not true. Neither is there any clue in the name. All cartridge papers are matt surfaced but anything called art surface or cast coated is likely to be very glossy. The only solution is to go to an artists' or drafting suppliers and look for yourself. Many black-surfaced cards and papers can also get a glossy sheen by being rubbed on the back of other sheets in the stack. Handle with care. There are also different densities of black and the cheaper ones have a decidedly grey look under your lights. Also, cheap white-surfaced boards and papers will not take colour so evenly.
- Animated graphics that use sliding segments need to be fabricated from six-sheet board (1275 microns).
- Sliding segment graphics will need a non-surfaced board of the same thickness as the seen board for use as spacer sheets. This is sometimes called pulp board.
- Drum, belt or mechanically moved graphics often need to use a robust paper, called cover paper, or a light card, which can wrap around a cylinder without crinkling or creasing.

Wiggins Teape has a good range of paper and boards but the suppliers I have found to have very suitable boards and papers are Daler-Rowney and Slater-Harrison. Daler-Rowney supply Studland mounting boards in a wide range of matt-surfaced colours including black and white in A1 size and six-sheet thickness. In addition they have a six-sheet pulp board, which can serve as a space sheet, as well as double-sided black boards. Their Canford card and cover papers are ideal for motorized graphics and lighter applications. Instead of using jet black surface you might like to try navy blue in Canford card and cover paper. This can actually look deeper and darker than black under certain lighting conditions. Those of you who have bought formal

Illustration 49

clothes for evening wear will know that a very dark blue looks blacker than black. Black itself can look powdery and sooty.

Slater-Harrison supply a very useful matt black and matt blue board called Studioline from their Televisual range. (See Suppliers' List.)

Photographs

Photographs can be used directly or cut up and collaged into an image. These should be good quality prints as there will be a reduction in quality when transferring them onto video. Use matt surface throughout and check that your photoprinter interprets matt, not silk or lustre. Glossy surfaces can give reflection problems but if you have invested in the polarizing sheets (see Chapter 1) you will be able to overcome these.

Sources of illustrations

For those of you whose drawing abilities are not yet fully developed there is a range of clip art available in book form and on disc for use with computers such as Apple Macs. This can be copied, modified and used as caption material. For those of you who can draw but can never get anyone to pose for you there is a range of photo source books called Fairburn Figures that are extremely comprehensive and show figures in all sorts of situations and poses. (See Graphic Books International in the Suppliers' List.)

Copying directly from other illustrations with a copier or by tracing, is an infringement of copyright and could result in legal action.

4   Mechanicals

Belt Titlers

A belt titler is simply an endless belt of material with the titles or graphics laid in the central portion. This gives various scrolling effects according to its running angle and the composition of the belt. The most common is a vertical scroll but long perspective effects can be got by massive belts many metres long, as used in the introduction to Star Wars.

The simplest way to make a belt titler is to use a drum titler that has the drum securely fixed to the turntable. This runs horizontally and the paper strip is hung down with a weighted jockey roller suspended in the bottom loop. A horizontal belt needs a stand for the jockey roller and a long Star Wars perspective effect needs a supporting table underneath the videoed area to maintain flatness and stability. Some method of ensuring good traction with the main drive is needed and an effective way is to paint two or three lines of rubber latex adhesive along the back. When dry this provides a flexible grip.

The paper belt itself can be made up from two sheets of cover paper butt joined at an angle to the direction of travel. Stick the join with Scotch Magic tape or brown PVC parcel tape on the underside. Arrange the graphic or titles so that the belt starts and stops with its join out of shot. This will probably entail having a lot more belt than is seen.

Unperforated paper sold in rolls for some types of computer printer is quite good; even wallpaper will work well, as will roller blind material.

The slatted belt titler in Figure 38 is quite easy to make and gives a different effect to the flexible belt. It is driven by a barbecue spit motor. These are cheap and easily obtainable and most seem to have a common fixing and drive system. However, as this is the part you cannot modify, it would be advisable to buy this first and make the rest of the titler to fit.

Next, the slats. I found that ready cut and finished Ramin strip 33 mm wide was ideal and accurate. This can be obtained from a woodwork or DIY shop. Cut it to eight 300 mm lengths.

Line up the eight pieces accurately; the slats should be butted together with no gap between them. Fix them temporarily in place with self-adhesive tape. Coat two strips of 50 mm-wide tape or bandage with a rubber latex adhesive such as Copydex and lay them on the back. Give an extra coat of latex when the first coat has dried. Remove the self-adhesive tape when the latex has set. Finally join the two ends with the same 50 mm-wide tape. It is important that the tape you choose has no lengthwise stretch. This will ensure that the slats hinge precisely and do not move apart.

You will also need three pieces of 45 × 18 mm wood cut to 305 mm to act as supports between the end pieces. The width and height are not critical but the length is, so that the drive shaft and slats do not bind against the end pieces. Cut two pieces of 8 mm-thick ply 155 × 250 mm to form the end plates. Clamp or tape them together and mark a centre line down from one short edge. Measure 44 mm down this line and drill a 1 mm pilot hole. Important: check these dimensions against your spit motor.

Offer up the wood you have cut for supports, mark around it, and drill and countersink the screw holes on both pieces. Separate the end pieces and enlarge one pilot hole to 25 mm diameter. This hole fits the raised portion at the front of the barbecue motor. Check yours for precise size and make the hole accordingly.

Enlarge the other pilot hole to 7 mm to take the round end of the drive shaft. You might like to place a proper bearing in here.

Cut a slot in the top of the end piece with the 25 mm hole in it. This is to take the spit motor holding stud.

Make up a square shaft 300 mm long with 32 mm-wide faces. The faces have to be a little smaller than the width of the slats so the whole thing runs smoothly. At one end of the shaft fix a 7 mm diameter shaft. At the other fit a square section shaft to suit the drive socket in the spit motor. Ensure that both are central and run accurately.

Assemble all together to check and adjust for fit and smooth running.

When all is satisfactory, dismantle the titler and give all parts two coats of matt black blackboard paint or cellulose car spray paint. Reassemble when dry.

Set the graphics on black or coloured card strips and stick them to the laths with a low tack adhesive. The spit motor is reversible so the graphics will run either way.

Books

How to bind a simple book for turning in shot

Titling by turning the pages of a book is a bit hackneyed but, like all things, depends on how well it is done and the content of the pages for its ultimate effect. The most versatile ready-made books to use are spiral-bound sketchbooks. The only disadvantage is that the spiral binding is rather eye catching if seen in shot. Also the pages do not turn like those of bound books. It is quite straightforward to bind up a series of pages into a book. This has the distinct advantage of setting you free to select varieties of paper for the pages. Each page can be worked on as a separate sheet. Assemble

(a)

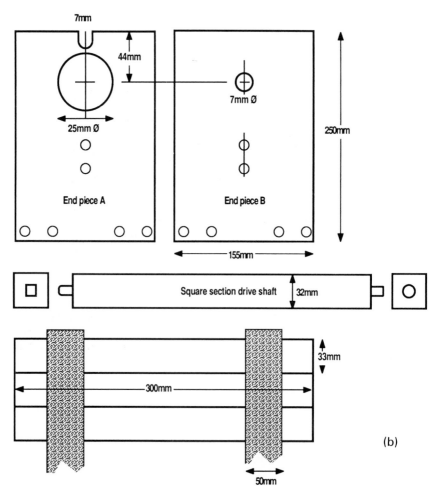

(b)

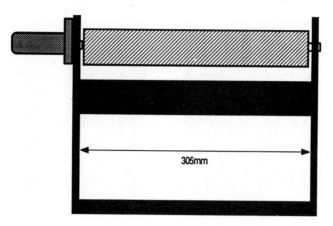

(c)

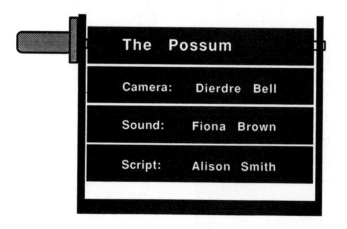

Figure 38 (a) Slatted belt titler.The black paper strips which carry the white lettering can just be made out in the photograph. In use the video camera can be set up to crush the black so that the strips are not seen. (b) and (c) Slatted belt titler construction.

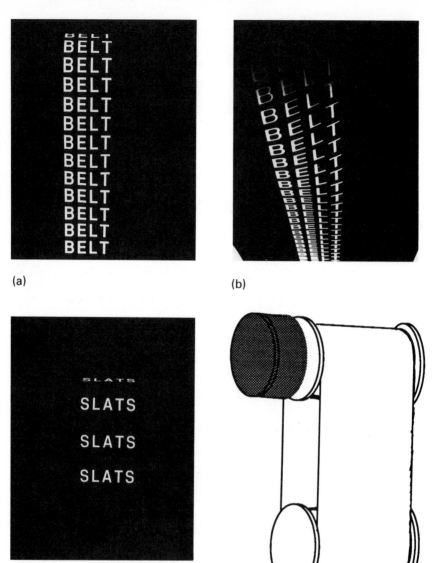

(a)   (b)

(c)   (d)

Figure 39 Effects of flexible and slatted belt titlers. (a) Paper belt with roll over at top on shot. (b) Paper belt twisted close to camera and run away in sharp perspective. (c) Slatted belt effect. (d) Simple belt titler run vertically. The bottom drum is undriven and rests in the loop of the belt to give tension.

them in order and the right way around. Add at least two blank pages, one at the beginning and one at the end, to simulate end papers. The final thing looks very authentic, especially if part of the bound edge is in shot. It is also a good way of making any kind of notebook or sketchbook.

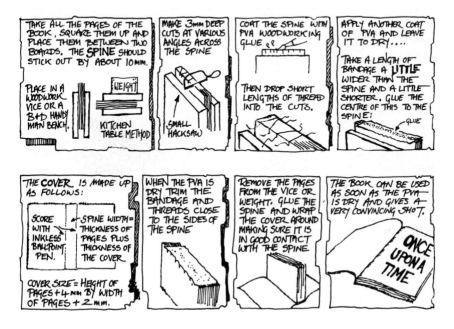

Figure 40 Binding a book for turning in shot.

Turning-page effect

The turning-page effect enables pages to be turned as in a book but, unlike in a book, the pages will always lie flat and turn smoothly and accurately.

This page-turning titler is essentially a set of very robust hinges to which caption cards can be temporarily attached. However, their construction is more subtle than a mere set of rings on a rod.

Figure 42a shows a set of hinges composed of short tubes mounted on a rod. This works reasonably well as long as the caption card material is quite thin. The cards rotate smoothly about the hinge axis. However, in this layout each caption card has its hinges mounted progressively closer together. A more satisfactory arrangement is shown in Figure 42b.

The problem with this is that if you need to use a more robust card, which does not flex when turning, the hinge mechanism will not allow the pages to lie flat. In order to allow for the thickness of card and give a flat surface to video, the hinges are made with offset card tabs. Figure 42c shows two ways

Figure 41 The screen effect of a page turner titler.

of making hinges which will hold a stack of card pages flat. The perspex version needs the use of a milling machine. It does not need to be made from perspex (in fact, thick brass tubing is very satisfactory); it is just that the walls of the tube need to be at least 3 mm thick to take the milling slots.

The bent strip versions can be made around a proprietary bending mandrel obtainable from model engineers' suppliers.

This titler will give the effect of text appearing as if on a page without the actual page or any part of the 'book' being seen. (See Figure 41.) The pages must be matt black on both sides and the page edges blackened. White or light-coloured lettering should be used.

Focus the camcorder on the centre page of the stack and lock the auto focus. Set the exposure to manual and the aperture to f11 or smaller. This should give you a depth of focus sufficient to hold all the pages sharp and avoid hunting for the auto focus while turning the pages. Check the focus on the first and last pages.

Light the caption evenly (see Even lighting, pp. 3–7) and set the exposure on a sheet of paper or card the same colour and tone as the lettering (see Exposure methods, pp. 10–11). You may have to alter the shutter speed of some cameras to get f11 or smaller.

Remove the exposure setting paper and video the pages as they are turned smoothly by hand.

The effect seen should have light lettering on a featureless black background turning up towards the viewer and revealing the page underneath.

Hint: Remember that the audience will be able to read and comprehend the text as it is in motion. Either turn it slowly with short static phases, or have longer static phases and turn quite quickly.

Magnetics

This is most often used where a chart, diagram or picture is built up on screen by a presenter. It can be very effective but take care over their placing and manufacture, as it is possible for the magnets to fail.

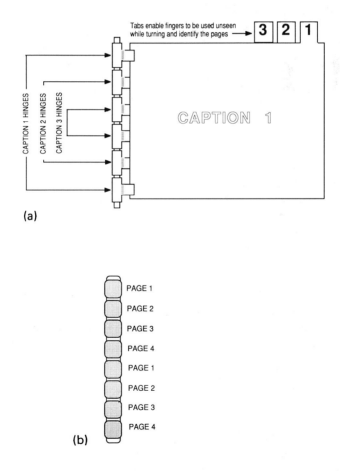

Figure 42 Page turner titler construction.

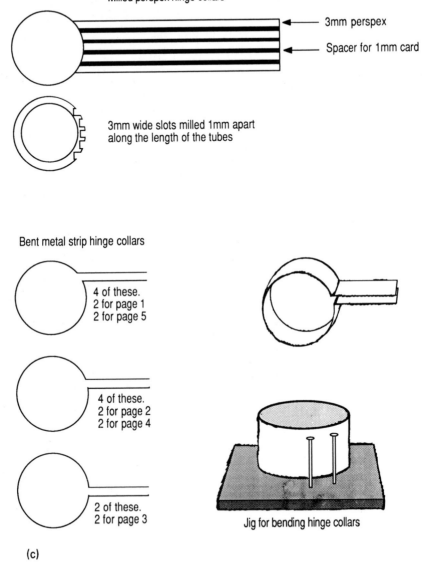

Milled perspex hinge collars

3mm perspex

Spacer for 1mm card

3mm wide slots milled 1mm apart
along the length of the tubes

Bent metal strip hinge collars

4 of these.
2 for page 1
2 for page 5

4 of these.
2 for page 2
2 for page 4

2 of these.
2 for page 3

Jig for bending hinge collars

(c)

Figure 42 Page turner titler construction.

Figure 42 Page turner titler construction.

The most reliable way to make a magnetic caption is to use a sheet of mild steel as a backing piece. A shelf from slotted angle shelving systems will do and there are specially made white boards available though these are rather expensive. An alternative is to use the door or sides of a fridge, cooker, deep-freeze, microwave etc. This is ready stove enamelled, too. If you want a different colour or effect then a background drawing or colour could be made on a sheet of thin paper that has been pasted onto the steel sheet.

Paste the paper before you do any drawing or colouring on it. Use cellulose wallpaper adhesive; the paper can easily be removed by rewetting it afterwards. Be sure to wet the paper thoroughly all over. Dry spots will show as blisters and wrinkles. Leave to soak in for a minute and then smooth the paper onto the steel. Allow to dry slowly so the paper can shrink and tighten gradually. Overnight would be fine. This ensures that the paper is tight to the steel and will not crease or waver when magnets are applied later. Make any drawing or colouring on the background when it is dry but be careful not to over-wet the paper. A very thin coat of matt varnish or pastel fixative applied before applying colour will help to seal the paper. Use drawing inks as these will stain the paper rather than add a possibly raised surface.

Draw and cut out the elements of the graphic that are to be placed on the background. Use a fairly stiff card such as Canford card. Spray both sides with a dead matt varnish or fixative that should dry invisibly. This prevents fingers marking the surface. It is unlikely your presenter or operator will get it right first time and will, anyway, need several rehearsals. The reason for spraying both sides is that the piece is likely to curl if you only treat one side.

Attach thin magnets to the back of each element with double-sided tape. Do not skimp this and use at least four. You can get thin plastic magnets from commercial stationers, who sell them for office organization charts.

Actually these types of graphic are quite effective even when the operator/presenter is not seen.

Paper engineering

This heading is a slight misnomer in that it implies that the only material you will need is paper. You will find that you might also need card, wire, various plastic fasteners, light wood and so on.

A graphic that contains various moving elements can be a very powerful device for explanation or effect. Usually it is not immediately evident to the audience that the image is anything other than a static illustration or lines of text. The animation then adds the elements of surprise and, hopefully, delight. Part of the fun in making and using these is the maintenance of this innocent deception through accurate cutting and careful construction combined with suitable lighting and camera work. This technique is often called Pugwash animation, after the children's Captain Pugwash TV cartoon programme.

It is worth taking a bit of care in manufacture for although the graphic may only be used once for one programme it is unlikely that all will go well when shooting and you will need to use it several times in rehearsal. Few things adversely affect reputation and stress more than a flimsy piece of paper engineering that performs well in rehearsal but expires during the shooting. This can also be very expensive too if people are kept hanging about as repairs are attempted.

Pivots

Pivotal points for card arms and levers are often made by the uninitiated from the ubiquitous brass-plated two-pronged paper fastener, which is highly unsuitable because:

- Its head is very noticeable.
- By nature it is a flat, sharp object trying to rotate in a round hole.
- The two-pronged tails catch in everything.
- It rapidly works loose.

There are two better solutions:

- Punch holes in both pieces and lightly clench them with an eyelet. You will need to use eyelet pliers to get the feel for how tight the clenching is going. Velos 950 combination punch and pliers are excellent for this. Eyelets can be bought in various colours and the drawing on the card can be so arranged as to disguise them from the camera.
- Use plastic snap fasteners that can be super glued or hot glue gunned to the card. Hot glue gives you time to position the fastener accurately. The moving parts can be brought quite close together to avoid undue shadows between them by marking around the two parts of the fastener and delaminating half the thickness of the card. Punching a snug hole for the clip part and sticking it flush with the surface of the card also works well. These have the advantage of being totally hidden from view. Buy the snap fasteners before you draw up the graphic so you can make the graphic fit the fastener. The most versatile fasteners I have found are Pikaby 6 × 15 mm. These are large enough to be manageable and have a small central hole in the stud portion so that thin piano wire crank extensions can be inserted easily and super glued in place. See Figure 43.

Eyelets and snap fasteners can be obtained from dressmaking, haberdashery or crafts shops.

Animated card graphic

This is an example of a simple animated concept which turned out to be quite an interesting problem. The requirement was for an animated graphic which demonstrated the way a water cistern ball valve worked.

The water level had to drop, the valve open, the water level rise and the valve shut. Obviously the ball valve float would need to be kept in contact with the water and pivoted at the valve body. The problem was that as the card depicting the water level dropped, the float described a horizontal line parallel to the water surface. This could be accommodated by cutting a slot in the water card and loosely fixing the float so that it ran captive in the slot. However, it was necessary to ensure that the slot would be always hidden by the float so that it did not spoil the illusion by appearing in shot. This was accomplished by a little empirical research using a card prototype. The size of the ball was varied, while retaining convincing size and geometry, until it completely masked the slot.

Assembly was not a logical progression from back to front as the ball had to be fixed to the water slider and the valve body. This needed access from both sides, which was impossible if the background card had already been stuck in place.

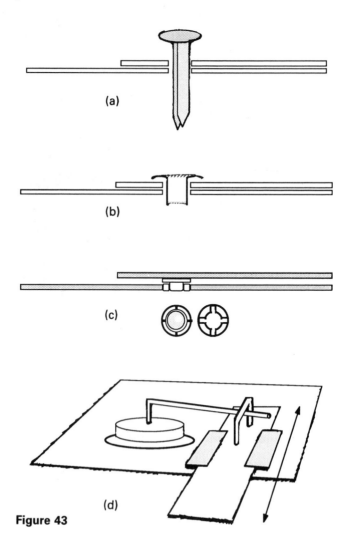

Figure 43

(e)

Figure 43 (*cont.*)

(f)

Figure 43 Types of paper pivots. (a) The paper fastener. Not suitable for moving pivots. (b) A lightly clenched eyelet. Quite good and a thin washer top and bottom improves things enormously. (c) Nylon snap fastener. Very good indeed for joining but especially valued for their pivoting action which has a robust and smooth action. (d) Piano wire inserted through the hole in a nylon snap fastener and extended to give a crank action with a sliding piece. (e) Front view of card animated dancing mouse. When the tab is pushed and pulled the head nods and the arms move apart and together. (f) Rear view of dancing mouse showing snap fastener pivots and piano wire cranks.

The first spacer pieces were stuck to the back of the second spacer and the water level slider placed snugly into the first spacer pieces gap. The water level sliders' arms extended from either side as operating handles. The edges of the water level slider ran smoothly on the edges of the first spacer, so preventing any unseemly movement of the water.

The second spacer was now glued to the back of the top sheet. The second spacer is to allow room for the valve arm to operate. The ball was lightly clenched with eyelets to fix it to the slot in the water level card and to the valve body.

Finally the background sheet was glued to the back.

Rotating Captions

Turntables

The essential basic piece of equipment for rotating captions is some form of powered turntable. Direct hand power makes it difficult to maintain a steady speed. Some form of hand cranking, well geared down, and with a heavy turntable to act as a flywheel and smooth out the irregularities of hand power, would be more effective.

Alternatives would be to use spring, weight or flywheel (gyro) driven motors. These are splendid. No electricity supply or batteries are needed, they are environmentally sound and they are very easy to adapt from old clocks or make up from scratch.

An old record player would seem to make an excellent turntable but it goes around too quickly. Even at 33 rev/min text moves too fast to be legible. However, the actual turntable and bearings might be useful and, depending on its drive system, enough gearing down may be possible.

Electric power driven turntables

The speed needed for comfortable viewing is around 2 to 4 rev/min and the most satisfactory way to achieve this steadily is with small electric motors:

- Use a mains-powered Crouzet motor, the sort used for the electro-mechanical timers and switches in washing machines. These can be obtained very cheaply from surplus shops. They are quite powerful and come with little gearboxes attached. However, they typically have a final output speed of around 24 rev/min and need to be geared down six times. This can be done by fitting a gear wheel with 10 teeth to the motor and a gear wheel with 60 teeth to the underside of the turntable, or pro rata. Alternatively use a friction drive as has been done with the one in Figure 45. This whole turntable was made from the running gear

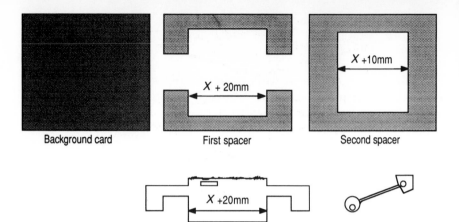

Background card	First spacer	Second spacer
	$X + 20$mm	$X +10$mm

Water level slider $X +20$mm

Ball cock and float

Use Cow Gum or double sided tape to glue the sheets together,
NOT a water based adhesive that causes the sheets to warp

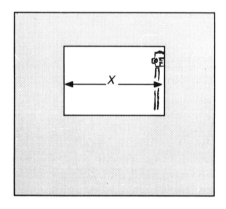

(a)

X

Top Sheet

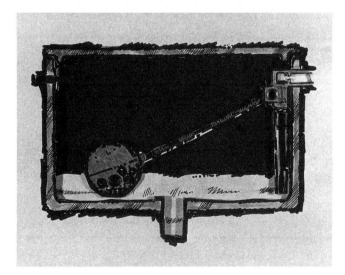

(c)

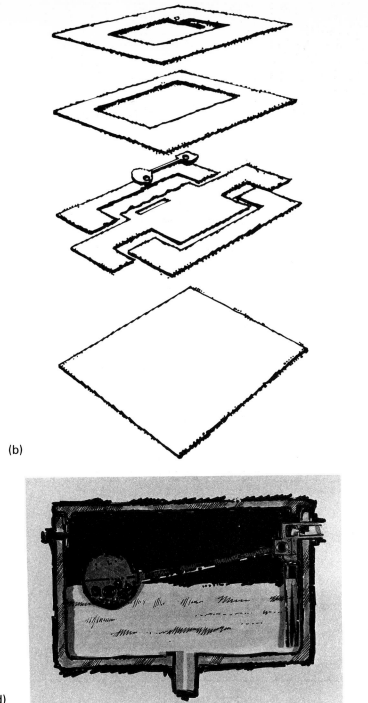

(b)

(d)

Figure 44 Mechanical animated cistern graphic. (a) Construction details.
(b) Assembly of the layers. (c) Finished graphic with low water level.
(d) Full.

(a)

(b)

of an old fruit machine. The spindles and bearings are all 10 mm diameter, far in excess of that necessary for the load it will carry but giving excellent stability. See Figure 46 for a cross-section of the bearing assembly. The base and the top and bottom drum caps are the fruit machine display wheels, with the picture strips removed, naturally.

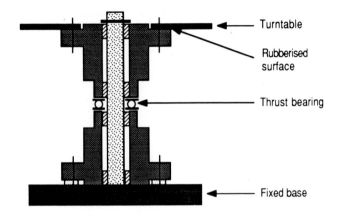

Figure 46 Cross-section of turntable spindle to show degree of engineering necessary for smooth action.

- Purchase a small battery-powered motor and gearbox kit, such as Como 431G, from modelmakers' suppliers or direct from Como Drills (see Suppliers' List). These have gearboxes that will give final speeds down to 2 rev/min according to the gear arrangement and input voltage you select. Being DC they can also be run in reverse by changing the polarity. (See Figure 47.)

The only problem with these is that they do not have thrust bearings on the final drive shaft, which means they will not stand up to very much downward pressure. Also, the final drive shaft bearings are plastic and can give an erratic effect on the turntable. It is best to use these run indirectly to a connecting drive onto the turntable. If you wish to use the final output shaft connected directly to the underside of a light turntable then a simple

Figure 45 A Crouzet motor driven turntable made from old fruit machine parts. (a) Close up of the motor drive. The base uses a complete fruit machine reel assembly with bearings. The top part of the bearings has a rubber tyre fitted. The Crouzet motor's drive wheel has been dipped in Plasti Dip® to give it a rubberized finish and a good grip on the rubber tyre. The motor is flexibly mounted and can be tensioned against the main drive wheel with the adjusting screw on the left. In use there is a safety cover around the motor drive area. (b) The turntable with an acetate sheet drum sandwiched between the two halves of a fruit machine reel.

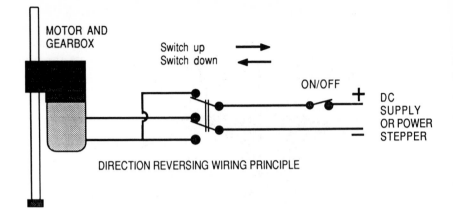

MOTOR AND
GEARBOX

Switch up →
Switch down ←

ON/OFF

\+ DC
SUPPLY
OR POWER
− STEPPER

DIRECTION REVERSING WIRING PRINCIPLE

DPDT SWITCHES WIRED FOR POLARITY CHANGEOVER

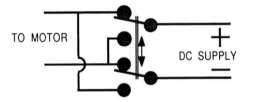

TO MOTOR

\+
DC SUPPLY
−

It is not easy to get three-pole double
throw switches as in the diagram above.
The solution is to wire the much more
common double-pole double-throw
(DPDT) switches as shown

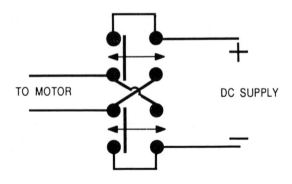

TO MOTOR

\+
DC SUPPLY
−

STANDARD TOGGLE DPDT SWITCH

Figure 47 DC motor direction-reversing switch.

(a)

(b)

Figure 48 A small battery-powered turntable using a Como motor and gearbox. (a) Front view showing motor, gearbox and thrust bearing. On the right, top to bottom: speed control, direction-changing switch and power on-off switch. (b) Rear view showing batteries and wiring.

thrust bearing can be made up with some 3 mm brass sleeving to steady the shaft. (See Figure 49.)

Reduction table for 431G motor and gearbox

No. of Gears	Rev/min at 1.5 V	Rev/min at 3.0 V	Rev/min at 4.5 V
6	2	4	6
5	5	10	14
4	16	32	45
3	44	88	125
2	150	300	410
1	400	800	1150

In the instructions they advise oiling the gearbox when assembled. In fact, light grease is better. These gearboxes are characteristically noisy when running.

Being battery powered this motor and gearbox are easily portable and have the added advantage of being reversible. Figure 47 shows a polarity changeover switch wiring diagram. They also operate over a range of voltage supply, typically 1.5–4.5 V. This gives the possibility of speed variations without altering the gear trains, which could be used while shooting. A simple voltage changer which will do this is shown in Figure 50. Wiring-up tip for the voltage changer: mount the direction changeover switch horizontally so the direction of the switch toggle indicates the direction of rotation. Wire up everything but leave the motor connection until last. Connect these loosely and switch on. Observe the direction the motor runs compared with the direction of the switch toggle. If this is the same then solder the wires in position. If it is opposite, reverse the motor wires and then solder.

The on-off switch is not strictly necessary as position 1 on the rotary switch is off but it is occasionally useful to have this. Alternatively you could replace it with a switched socket for a remote control.

- A barbecue spit motor can be obtained very cheaply, especially in winter! These typically run off a 1.5 V battery, have a built-in reverse-direction switch and turn at 5 rev/min. The output is a 7 mm-square hole to take the barbecue spit. This will not take a vertical loading as the shaft rubs on the rear of the gearbox casing and the gearbox itself is quite flimsy. However, it runs well horizontally, as it was designed to do, and will drive slatted titling belts and similar horizontal titlers.

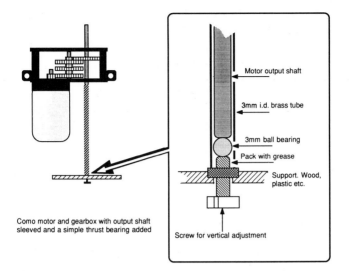

Como motor and gearbox with output shaft sleeved and a simple thrust bearing added

Motor output shaft

3mm i.d. brass tube

3mm ball bearing

Pack with grease

Support. Wood, plastic etc.

Screw for vertical adjustment

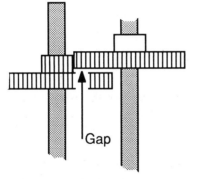

Gap

Fix the motor to its support. Adjust the thrust bearing screw until there is a slight gap between the output shaft gear and the final gear in the gearbox

This ensures that any vertical load will not cause the two gears to bind together on their faces

Figure 49 The thrust bearing used with the Como motor and gearbox.

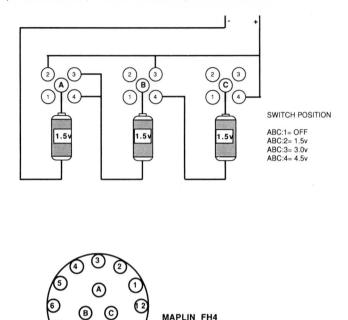

Figure 50 This power stepper gives a variable control over the speed of the turntable, using a three-pole, four-position rotary switch. Maplin sells a suitable rotary switch, Cat No: FH44, as does Electrovalue, Cat. No.: SR34. The back of these look like the lower diagram. Substitute the numbers on the individual switch contacts in the upper diagram for the ones on the FH44 switch. A: 1,2,3,4. B: 5,6,7,8. C: 9,10,11,12. For a continuously variable control a CMOS circuit should be used. A simple variable resistance is very inefficient. A CMOS/FET speed controller is quite easy to build but is quicker to buy ready assembled from Proops Distributors or Maplin supplies (see Suppliers' list).

Turntable construction

The actual turntable can be cut from any stable material such as 3−5 mm plywood or perspex. The main problem is to get the turntable running true on the shaft and one effective way to do this is to start by making or buying something that will make a suitable collar. A pulley or gear wheel that fits the shaft and has a flat face will work well. Otherwise a custom-made one can be turned up in a lathe from plastic or light metal.

Take the sheet of material chosen for the turntable. Fix the spindle collar to the centre of the sheet. Place a rod in the collar and draw around it with a

Figure 51 A barbecue spit motor.

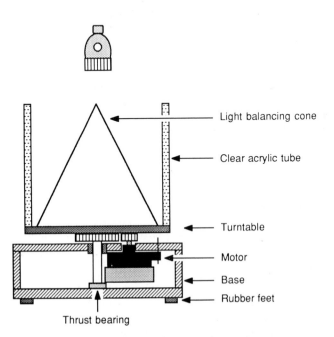

Light balancing cone

Clear acrylic tube

Turntable

Motor

Base

Rubber feet

Thrust bearing

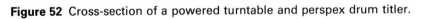

Figure 52 Cross-section of a powered turntable and perspex drum titler.

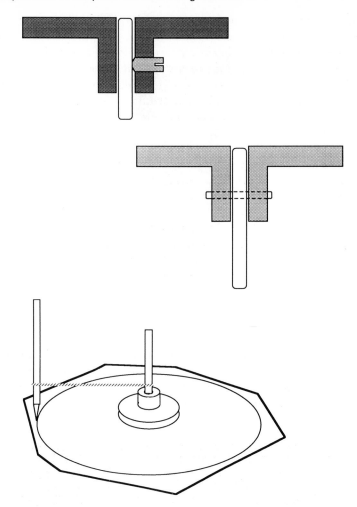

Figure 53 Marking out the turntable and fixing it to the shaft. Top: Grubscrew. (Most pulley wheels are supplied with a grubscrew.) Middle: Pin drive. A hole is drilled through the shaft and a tight-fitting pin driven through so that it extends both sides of the shaft by at least 3 mm. A corresponding slot is cut in the turntable flange. This drops over the pin, allowing you to remove the turntable easily yet retain a positive drive. Bottom: Marking out a turntable from the fixed collar. Tie the string lightly to the pencil and shaft so that it can move around both as it is turned. Otherwise it will wind up around the pencil and/or shaft and give an inaccurate circle. Keep the pencil vertical as you move it around.

pencil attached to the rod with a piece of string. This will give you a circular turntable trued up on the centre spindle. Cut this out carefully. The most effective way is with a circle-cutting attachment on a small bandsaw.

The larger the diameter of the turntable shaft the better. A 3/8th-inch or 9 mm shaft is excellent. It may seem over-engineered for the light work involved but the size gives solidity and stability. I used the bearings and shaft from an old fruit machine for one and it has a very satisfactory smoothness and robustness.

The turntable spindle must rest on a thrust bearing. This can be as simple as doming the end of the spindle and resting it in a greased cup of similar diameter, preferably brass. Alternatively you may go the whole hog and get a ball thrust race from a model makers' shop or bearing suppliers, or use one from that old record player.

Alternatively you could obtain a window display turntable. These run quite slowly and use an eddy current motor like that found inside an electric meter. Some have variable speeds.

Important: Do remember to earth all mains equipment.

Disc

Captions are applied to a flat sheet and rotated in front of the camera. The disc can be laid on the turntable or on the end of a drum titler.

According to how they are set on the sheet, captions will curve up from the bottom or swoop down from the top.

Figure 54 Effect of titles on a disc titler.

Drum

A drum titler produces rolling captions where the text or graphic appears to be rolling around the surface of a cylinder which is rotated on a turntable.

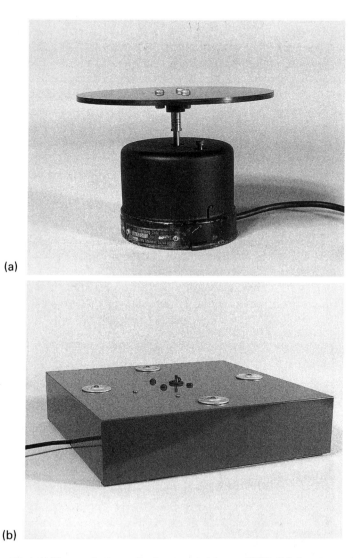

(a)

(b)

Figure 55 (a) Shop window display turntable. *c.* 1940. (b) Large motorized turntable. The table has been removed to show the supporting ball roller bearings. This uses a slightly different principle in that the load is carried on the balls, not on the spindle. This also makes it more stable and is suitable for larger turntables.

With suitable exposure the captions can appear to be suspended in space. (See Exposure methods, pp. 10–11, and Figure 58.)

An actual drum is needed and this can either sit on the turntable or be securely fixed to the motor base. The latter is preferable if making one from scratch as it can then be run in the horizontal position. This gives you the choice of vertical rolling captions as well as horizontal and all angles between if you wish. It helps if the top and bottom caps to the drum are slightly larger in diameter than the drum itself, say about 2 cm. This makes a flange that not only helps with registration of successive artwork but also guides the longer strips of paper needed if using the drum to drive a belt titler.

A ready made drum such as a large can, tube or pipe is suitable. It is important to use a rigid material so that the title is held firm. The diameter of the drum should not be less than about 100 mm. If it is, the text has to be correspondingly smaller (not a good thing with video), the curvature is very pronounced and the whole exercise becomes very difficult to frame.

My favourite is a piece of 150 mm diameter clear acrylic tubing with a 6 mm-thick wall. This gives the necessary rigidity and allows backlit effects with coloured lights or gels. However, this is quite expensive and quite difficult to get hold of in short lengths. At the time of writing the minimum length supplied of 200 mm diameter was 2.5 m and with a 3.5 mm wall this cost £168 plus VAT! Try perspex stockists for offcuts as well as exhibition stand manufacturers and industrial model makers. You only need a length of around 300 mm.

Alternatively you might like to try to roll up your own clear drum. This needs patience and ingenuity.

Cut a pair of end cap discs from perspex, chipboard or plywood approximately 200 mm in diameter. These should have a lip around the edge. (See Chapter 3.)

Cut a strip of 0.25-mm-thick clear acetate 900 mm wide by as long as you need to wrap around twice inside your finished discs. Acetate can be obtained from drafting or artists' suppliers in A0 sheets. Alternatively Draka Polva can supply clear Dulis plastic sheet of 0.4 mm (see Suppliers' List). Clean the sheet, a frustrating job as it charges up with static and attracts more than you are trying to remove. Wrap this inside one end cap, allowing the natural spring of the material to hold it inside the lip. Ensure it is snug against the lip and place the other end cap on top. Check for fit. The outside end will belly out in the middle. Carefully tape this down along its whole length with a light adhesive tape such as Post-It® or drafting tape. The inner end should be held flush with the wall of acetate by tension but check this then tape it lightly down.

Gently run some plastic weld cement or similar (obtainable from EMA Model Supplies or your local model shop) along the top edge. This has a high capillary action and runs down between the layers. This sets very quickly, welding the acetate together. Gently peel the adhesive tapes off, running plastic weld in along the exposed edge as you go. Turn the drum over and repeat along the other edge. Finally glue the end caps in place. The resulting drum is not as rigid as cast acrylic tube but it works quite well.

To take advantage of a clear drum you will need to use clear or transparently coloured graphics on opaque sheets, such as Omnichroms or Cibachromes or large Liths. Sometimes a diffuser sheet of plastic paper is needed to even out the light if a bulb is suspended inside the drum. A simple cone of white paper will evenly distribute the light from an overhead source. Clear material is preferable to white translucent as it is more versatile and can always be made translucent, whereas white translucent is, well, white translucent all the time. A shield should be put immediately behind the drum to prevent the light spill from the lettering on the rear of the drum shining onto the background.

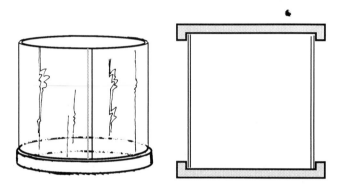

Figure 56 Thin acetate drum with supporting end caps.

If backlighting is not important then it is possible to obtain orange PVC piping at a very useful 200 mm outside diameter. Unfortunately it comes in very expensive 6 m lengths that, at the time of writing, were around £100 each. This does not make the exercise economically viable for a one-off, or enter into the spirit of this book. Plastic pipework manufacturers (see Yellow Pages) may, however, let you have some offcuts. A piece of this pipe around 900 mm long would be ideal. EMA will sell shorter lengths.

Set the captions in dry transfer lettering on a dead matt paper, such as Canford cover paper from Daler-Rowney. Fix these securely to the drum with a low tack adhesive such as Pelikan RollFix Temporary. Set the drum up at least 1 m from the background and light it carefully. (See pp. 3–10.)

Starting with the captions on the side away from you run the camera and drum. Continue until the captions disappear around the other side. Pause the camera, change captions if necessary and continue as before.

Other applications and effects can be obtained by experimentation; in this way you begin to gather a personal inventory of visuals.

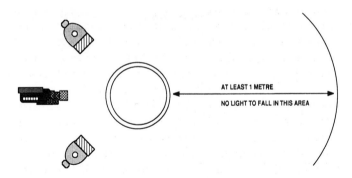

Figure 57 Top view of camcorder and titling drum set up to give a featureless black background.

Cube

This method is essentially the same as that using a drum except that a solid cube is used. This has to be carefully made so that it is rigid and it is worth spending some time on this if a ready-made cube cannot be found. A face width of 100 mm should be regarded as minimum.

The effect is of facets of text and graphics rotating in space and with good lighting and exposure these will appear to be suspended in space without the supporting cube being seen.

Figure 58 Effect of titles on a drum titler run horizontally.

Figure 59 Effect of titles on a cube titler.

The cube can be rotated on one face or by a corner. Of course, only four changing captions can be got but with a bit of camera movement the top face can also be brought into shot.

Vane Titler

This is a sort of reversed cube with the caption cards slotted together and placed on a turntable. The effect can be similar to the page-turning effect, though you are limited to six cards per shoot, otherwise they are too close together.

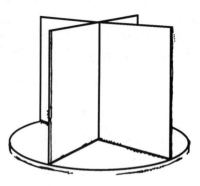

Figure 60 Vane titler.

Sand and powder captions

Wet, scratched in and built up. Wash away.

If you found that the actual sand on the beach was a bit uncontrollable, as was the weather, the light and the other beach users, wait until you get home to put the finishing touches to your holiday videos. Put some damp sand into a shallow dish and smooth it into a convincing 'water's edge' effect. Scratch your graphics into the sand with a piece of sharp stick.

Place the finished sandy graphics on the copystand and light them very directionally so the texture is thrown into sharp relief. You can make a convincing 'tide wash' by adding odd flotsam to slightly soapy water.

Alternatively the graphic can be built up using wet dribbled sand or beach flotsam; the point is that this is all under control in the studio. Do take care to keep sand and water well away from lights and equipment and wipe your hands well before handling the camcorder or loading a tape.

Figure 61 Titling scratched into damp sand.

Dry blow away, 3D reveal and adhesive reveal

Dry sand may be blown away to reveal a title under the sand. The object to be discovered can be specially made from wooden letters, plastic or glassfibre, foam core board, Fimo modelling plastic etc. It could be an actual object such as a bottle, scroll, tin lid etc. with an appropriate paper label attached.

Actual sand is nasty to have blowing around, even out of doors, and heavy unless you sieve it well and only use the finest grains. It helps to move the sand if the whole setup is tilted slightly so that gravity assists the blowing. A hair dryer, or the reverse end of a vacuum cleaner, will work well but do this out of doors. One alternative is to use fine sawdust, though this can lack the convincing mass of sand.

Figure 62 Dry sand blown away to reveal titles

At the other end of the mass scale is gardening vermiculite or polystyrene balls for bean bags. These can be very lively and blow everywhere. Use a large open bin liner to catch what you can.

An adhesive reveal is where the graphics are painted on a background in glue and liberally dusted over with dry sand, sawdust etc. while they are wet. Very accurate letterforms can be got by preparing the artwork on paper, making a photosilkscreen from this and screen printing them onto the background, dusting them immediately with fine sand, sawdust etc. Polystyrene balls and vermiculite are a bit coarse in grain size to hold the detail for this technique. Alternatively you could cut the letters out of sand paper and stick them onto another background sheet.

The whole thing is buried in sand that is then blown away to reveal the graphics. Directional lighting shows this effect up well.

Sliders

Simple slider

Sliders are amongst the easiest and most effective animated graphics to make. As with all animations it is worth devoting a little extra care to design and manufacture to ensure smooth, lurch-free movement.

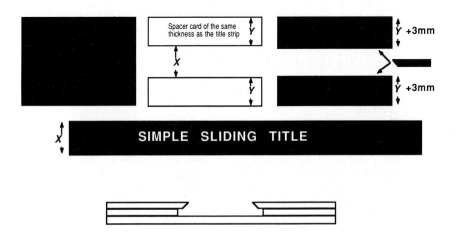

Figure 63 Basic sliding graphic construction.

Take a sheet of black mounting board (Daler six-sheet double-sided black is ideal), large enough to fill completely the frame of your video camera when focussed at a convenient working distance. An A4 sheet will fill the frame of most video cameras and still give a comfortable working distance. (See Proportions and useful working sizes, pp. 28–30.)

Cut a long strip of black mounting board for the actual slider. Just how long and how wide this needs to be will depend upon the actual title or graphic size you intend to use. If you want the title to slide onto a blank screen or disappear, leaving a blank screen, then there will need to be a screen width and a half of extra card before and/or after the title.

Cut two strips of six-sheet pulp board to act as guides and spacers. You can use the six-sheet mounting board for this but it seems a bit of a waste.

Place the sliding strip in the centre of the backing card. Apply adhesive to the back of the spacer pieces (see Basic materials, pp. 46–47). Butt them snugly up to the slider and press into position. Make sure that the slider moves for its full length of travel with no jerkiness.

Cut two pieces of black card the same length as the spacer pieces but 3 mm wider. Give the edge that will overlap the slider an undercut of around 45° and blacken it with a felt-tipped pen.

Apply adhesive to the underside of these pieces, except the 3 mm strip along the undercut side so as not to impede the movement of the slider. Align with the top and sides of the main card and press into position.

This simple device can be re-used many times simply by replacing the sliding strip with the current programme's details.

In operation this should be moved very smoothly. Even though this device is hand operated, a little practice will quickly result in a smooth movement. Ensure a smooth action by smoothing the mating edges and coating them with graphite from a soft pencil or spraying them with a dry PTFE lubricant. Some back tension is very helpful; a weight on a string attached to the opposite end of the slider gives you some slight substance to pull against, as the card alone is very light.

Sliding Reveal

This uses essentially the same principle as the simple slider except that the spacer pieces are of double thickness. Attach the caption or graphic to the base with low tack adhesive. The slider must have the revealing edge undercut by 45° and blackened with a felt-tipped pen. If using dry transfer lettering it should be sprayed with a matt fixative to prevent the underside of the slider marking it.

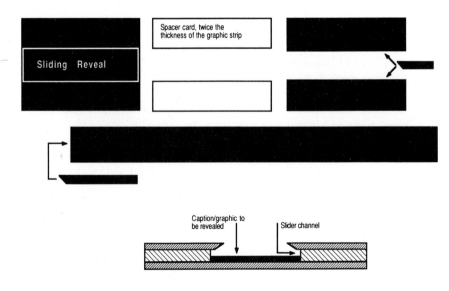

Figure 64 Sliding reveal.

Some back tension and dry lubricant on the bearing edges will aid smooth movement. (See Simple slider, p. 85.)

Universal Slider

This design combines the effects of the simple slider and the sliding reveal in one unit. It can be quite successfully made from six-sheet double-sided black Daler board but do remember to blacken all the cut edges with a black felt-tip pen. Use cow gum or another spirit-based adhesive to fix all the sheets together.

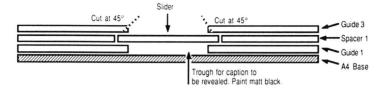

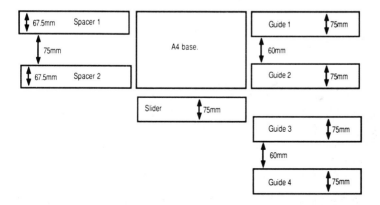

Figure 65 Universal slider.

Graphics can be done on black Canford card and attached to the slider, or drawn on six-sheet board and placed in the trough. Fix them in place with low tack adhesive. In this way you can re-use the basic mechanism and only need to replace the artwork.

You might consider it worth making this device in thin ply or plastic. Ensure that there is enough thickness in the spacers to allow for six-sheet or Canford card to be attached to the slider or slider base. In this case you would find it an improvement to fit light leaf pressure springs underneath the uppermost guides to grip the slider gently and provide good back tension. This prevents juddering of the slider.

Velcro boards

These have essentially the same use and effect as magnetics except that the background is a looped nylon material and the magnets are replaced by Velcro hook patches. The nylon material is difficult to paint effectively as paint tends to clog up the loops of the material and the Velcro hooks will not grip. However, if you use a light-coloured nylon and a thin intense colour such as waterproof drawing inks or liquid acrylic colour then some lovely effects can be achieved. This is for colouring certain areas, of course, not mass colouring the whole piece.

Figure 66 Velcro board.

Fix the background material to a rigid board with Copydex or a slightly diluted PVA glue such as Evostik Resin W. Do not apply the glue too liberally or it will appear through the weave of the fabric but make sure all the area is covered and there are no dry spots that could wrinkle or belly out under the weight of a graphic.

This sort of graphic is very effective when used within a programme with a presenter who can talk the graphics into place and interact with them.

Be careful when removing the graphic. Velcro grips very securely and rough handling can tear the graphic. It is not necessary to use large areas of Velcro; quite small pieces will hold securely enough.

Models

Small models with the appropriate titling on them can be very effective as they not only convey the information but also set the mood precisely. The problem for the video director is to ensure that the audience read them as titles. This is a matter of presentation and emphasis.

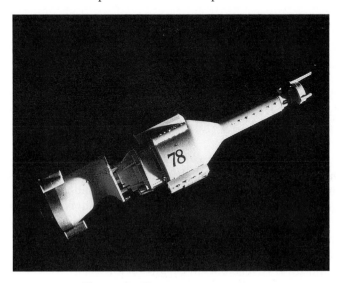

Figure 67 The space tramp '78'.

Figure 67 shows the spaceship '78' that was constructed from various pieces of scrap. It started life as a burned-out Braun hand blender; the body shells of this were rearranged and extra pieces from the 'too good to throw away' box were added. The whole thing was sprayed with grey car body primer to unify it, then distressed to give it the look of having been in space for many years. The numbering is dry transfer. Finally it was suspended with very fine black painted nylon line about a metre away from a black background. It was lit harshly using a slide projector with a card slide in the gate in which a 10 mm hole had been cut to restrict the light to the spaceship area. Thus no light fell on the background and full blackness was retained there.

In use the 78 was held very close in shot and only on the zoom-out did the audience realize that it was painted on the side of a spaceship: an old device but an effective one.

Holding the model still with piano wire mounted into the blind side and zooming, or tracking, the camera back underneath it will give the impression of the spaceship flying in overhead. The steadiness of movement this gives is much more satisfactory than trying to move the model, which always seems to twitch about in a very unrealistic way due to its lightness and scale.

5 Opticals

Animatics

The term refers to a technically unrefined type of animation. It is used by makers of television commercials to give the client a more complete idea of the finished production than could be gained from a storyboard.

In essence it consists of videoing a sequence of drawings in short bursts using the camcorder's release button. This can be a very hit and miss affair regarding frame accuracy but surprisingly acceptable results can be obtained. The general quality is somewhat jerky and the sequencing of the drawings should be designed to suit.

Familiarity with the characteristics of your camcorder will help get smoother actions. One of these characteristics that you need to discover is how much back space edit it performs after each shot.

To get a clean start or noiseless break between shots the camcorder runs back a few frames over the end of the previous shot immediately after you press the pause or stop button. This shortens the previous shot by a second or so. Of course this is not usually noticeable on normal shooting because you should always overshoot any scene at both ends by five seconds or so to compensate for this. With shot lengths as short as two seconds, losing 1.5 seconds or more could be a problem. This is why you need to know how much back space edit your camcorder performs and how reliable it is at maintaining this amount.

On many camcorders you will see the counter run back a few seconds as you press the pause button. You could use the counter to gauge back space edit if it showed tenths of a second, or a better way is to video a running stopwatch that will register tenths of a second. Do this in five-second bursts starting each burst when the second hand is at the top. To give yourself and the camcorder some time to sort yourselves out try this pattern:

- Set the stopwatch to zero.
- Set the camcorder on pause/record.
- Run the stopwatch.
- Wait until the stopwatch approaches 30 seconds.
- Release pause exactly on 30 seconds and press pause again on 35 seconds.
- Wait until the stopwatch approaches 60 seconds.
- Release pause exactly on 60 seconds and press pause again on 65 seconds and so on for around ten shots.

View the result. You will find that the stopwatch never shows a full five-second shot on screen; mostly each shot will be shorter by a second or so at the end. Sometimes the camcorder is slow in starting up so the shot starts into the action. This combination of losing a bit at the beginning as well as the end is not a disaster, provided you know how much and, most important, if it is consistent. The Hi8 camcorders have very economical and reliable back space edit.

When you have determined your losses it is a simple matter to add these onto your actual animatic shot length.

Make up a series of drawings, place them on a copystand and shoot them in short bursts. The more accurate your calculations and equipment and yourself at pressing and releasing the pause/record button, the smoother the action.

Figure 68 The drawings for an animatic (above) are not so concerned with portraying movement as those for an animation (below).

It is all a bit hit and miss but a lot of fun and the results are instantly viewable. Those of you who would like to try real frame by frame accurate animation need to make a substantial investment in an animation controller and appropriate U-Matic-type record and playback machines or a video line animation set-up that is computer controlled.

Some Camcorders, such as the Sony CCD V800 Hi8, have an animation facility whereby the camcorder will automatically record around four frames at each trigger release, with automatic allowance made for the loss with back space edit. This can give quite smooth animation if the movements between exposures are small. It is good enough for animation line testing to check a movement sequence and for piloting more ambitious works. The opportunities for titling and graphics are considerable. The trick is to work with the system and produce graphics which utilise the characteristics of the medium, rather than try to achieve something it was never designed to do. (See Chromacolour Animation Supplies in the Suppliers' List.)

Filters

There are a variety of commercial filters with all sorts of effects in the Cokin and Cromatek range. This is all very helpful and fast but unoriginal. Most types of filters are amongst the easiest things to make and their effect can be judged in a coupled monitor as you work. The effects you get are your own; no-one else can go and buy one.

Start with a Cokin or Cromatek filter holder and screw in the adaptor for your camcorder. The filter holders are two- or three-sided boxes and take an acrylic filter 2.5−3 mm thick. Offcuts of clear or coloured Perspex™ or Lexan™ in these thicknesses can be obtained from sign makers, plastic fabricators, and model builders and cut to fit. Alternatively you could use some pieces of picture glass. This is thinner than window glass and can be cut to size by glass merchants or picture framers. The sharp edges can be ground down on an oilstone. Non-reflecting glass makes a good ready-made diffusion filter.

Clear blanks in glass or acrylic can then be treated in the following ways.

Diffusion Filter

Most of the proprietary diffusion filters are just too weak for really dramatic effects. However, a diffusion filter can be made quickly and easily and in a

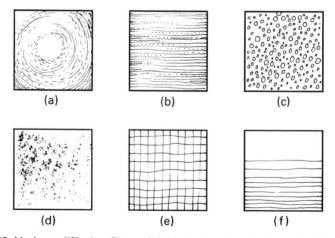

Figure 69 Various diffusion filters. (a) Vaseline wiped on in a circular motion with centre clear. (b) Vaseline streaked on in a linear fashion. (c) Small dots of clear nail varnish. This gives a permanent finish. (d) White acrylic paint sprayed on. (e) Light scrim. (f) Parallel threads stretched across the filter holder, getting wider apart towards the centre.

variety of intensities. A heavy star filter, that is one that gives 16-point stars, will also work as a moderate diffusion or softening filter.

Part colour filter

These have a transparent colour applied over half the filter. This colour fades out gradually at the centre. To be honest it is a waste of your time trying to emulate the gentle gradations that are available commercially. However, there are other ways to get a similar effect and use stronger colours. The filter is so close to the lens that gradation to this degree of softness is not always necessary. Using colours that are very intense can produce unsatisfactory images under auto exposure. The meter equates between the filtered and unfiltered areas to such a degree that the result is a poor compromise. Put the camcorder on manual exposure and set the aperture according to the effect you want when viewed in the monitor. Very intense colours might be rendered very dark even with a manual set-up.

I have experimented with several types of transparent lacquers for glass and acrylic surfaces and among the most satisfactory have been those based on white spirit, cellulose and xylene. The white-spirit-based lacquers dry more slowly and so tend to flow rather more than the others. This makes them more suitable for application by brush, as the brush marks flow out, but less suitable for dotting on, as the dots tend to flow together. Cellulose lacquers can eat into the surface of acrylics such as Lexan™ though Perspex™ seems immune. Xylene-based lacquers are very quick drying and give good results, though the solvent is more hazardous to use and store.

Fantasy Dip-It film from handicraft shops has potential both as a filter film in its own right suspended across a wire frame and as a colour applied directly to glass or plastic sheet. The tins it is supplied in are a little small for normal filter sizes and it needs to be decanted into a jar with a wider mouth for dipping.

Multiple image

It's all done with mirrors and lenses. Much can be done with strips and pieces of mirror from quite unlikely sources, as is explained later in this chapter.

A visit to your local optician's lens grinding lab could turn up some interesting reject lenses. If these are cemented together edge to edge in various combinations some quite odd effects can be achieved, and they are unique to you! They may even grind facets on lenses to produce multiple image filters for you. Alternatively you can try yourself if you have access to a lapidary lapping wheel. Proprietary filters are the easiest method of

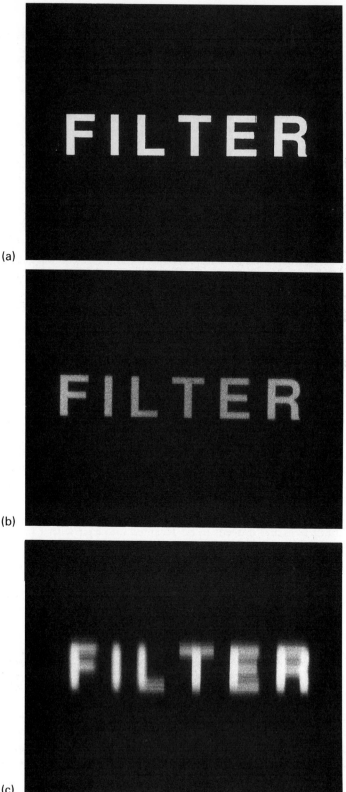

(a)

(b)

(c)

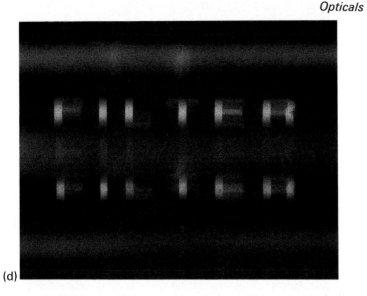

(d)

Figure 70 Effects through various diffusion filters. (a) Unfiltered. (b) Heavy clear nail varnish soft filter. (c) Acrylic cylinder filter. Bottles will sometimes do as well! (d) Filter made from two small clear acrylic tubes. In both (c) and (d) the camera shoots through the walls of the tube rather than down the middle.

achieving multiple image effects, but simply because of this they become a readily recognized effect very quickly. Try for something new and different.

Often multiple images are more intriguing if they are recorded out of focus and used in combination with crisp, superimposed graphics. Then they take on an abstract quality which does not invite such close critical inspection from the audience. The considered use of colour is a definite advantage here as the soft interplay of shapes produces exciting and interesting colour effects.

Effective multiple images can be produced using a lith slide in a 35 mm projector which is projected via a conventional mirror onto the back of a

Figure 71 Part colour filters. Ways of achieving interesting gradations. Left to right: from solid colour to clear by coarse spray or series of hand brush dots; from solid colour to clear by a series of fine lines of diminishing width; from solid colour to clear by a succession of bands, each of a thinner coat.

Figure 72 Multiple image filter. The left-hand half is composed of a 'lens' cut vertically in half with longitudinal plane facets in the upper surface. The right-hand half is open. The camcorder sees a normal image through the open half with repeat images formed by the faceted lens over the remainder.

piece of float glass which is frosted on one side. The camcorder shoots from the frosted side and the result is a strong sharp central image surrounded by secondary images formed from the surfaces of the mirror and the piece of frosted glass. The distances between the secondary images can be altered by changing the distances between the various components.

Star filter

The proprietary ones are regular and geometrically precise. If you want something with more character try engraving your own. This can be done

Figure 73 Effect of multiple image filter.

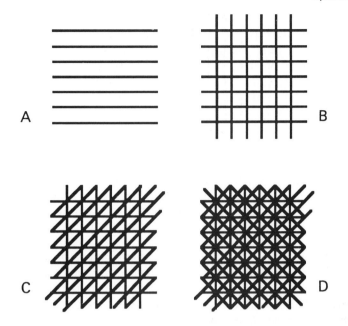

Figure 74 Typical star filter grids. A: Streak. B: Four-pointed star. C: Six-pointed star. D: Eight-pointed star.

quite easily by lightly scratching the surface of a sheet of acrylic with the point of a compass or the back of a scalpel blade. The grids in Figure 74 give conventional stars or streaks; you could try varying the angles slightly as you work. The most usual basic grid used is around 2 mm, but you could try varying this. You get slightly different results with different apertures, too. Just as with still cameras the trick is to set up the exposure meter without the star filter in place and then lock the exposure setting and place the filter on the lens. The reason for this is that with the filter in place and star streaks moving all over the place the meter thinks there is more light than there actually is. It quite rightly sets a correspondingly smaller aperture that gives correctly exposed stars, **just** what we want, with a gloomy underexposed main scene.

Mirrors

An awful lot can be done with mirrors. The following uses will give some idea. When you have some mirrors you can experiment away happily. Some tips: certain effects look better if the mirror is either very thin or, better still, surface silvered. With this type of mirror you do not get a secondary image from the surface of the glass. Surface-silvered mirrors are a bit specialist but can be obtained quite cheaply from mirror silverers who just leave the protective backing off. Unfortunately they begin to tarnish after a while. A more convenient solution is to buy the replacement mirror glass for car mirrors. For some makes of car, such as the Ford Granada, the glass is surface silvered. It can also be slightly reducing, which will give other wondrous effects.

Inexpensive slatted mirror placemats can be used as effects mirrors with wonderful results. It's all about being able to see possibilities in unlikely objects.

Mirror wipe

Scene A is set up to be shot via a mirror. Scene B is set up behind the mirror. Both should be optically at the same distance from the camcorder so no change in focus is required. At the dramatic moment of transition the mirror is slid gently and smoothly away. Scene B replaces Scene A as a wipe.

Because the mirror is out of focus the travelling edge is resolved as a smooth blur. Mount the mirror in a frame twice its length. It runs in plastic sliding cupboard door tracks and might need to be padded up a little so it does not move from side to side as it travels. A handle on the leading edge and some gentle back tension in the form of a rubber band against which to pull will help give a smooth action. (See Figure 75).

Kaleidoscope

This is very simple to make. Essentially, it consists of three long narrow mirrors taped together in a triangle with the reflecting surfaces inside. Figure 76 was taken down a more exciting tube consisting of ten strips of mirror 25 mm wide by 300 mm long. These were taken from a mirrored placemat; the backing was cut off and replaced with bandage fixed in place with latex carpet adhesive. This gave sufficient flexibility to allow the strips to be bent into a rough circle with the mirrors facing inwards and enough firmness to hold them all in place.

Interesting moving effects can be got by combining a kaleidoscope with a mechanical titler.

Mirror tube

This is essentially similar to a kaleidoscope except that the mirror is metallized melinex film which can be found in gift shops, fancy paper suppliers or craft shops. Choose a card tube big enough to fit neatly over the lens of your camcorder. About 300 mm long will be sufficient. The longer you have it the smaller the area you have to play with for the actual titling or graphic. Cut a piece of plastic mirror so that it will completely cover the inside of the card tube when rolled up, but is about 20 mm shorter than the tube length. Roll up the mirror and slip it inside the card tube. Adjust it so that it is flush with one end of the card tube. It will be about 20 mm short at the other end, that is the end you slip over the camcorder lens. The natural tension will hold the mirror in place but a dab of clear multi-purpose adhesive between the mirror and the card tube will prevent the mirror sliding out at a crucial moment.

As with the kaleidoscope, movement in the graphic produces interesting visual effects. Unlike the kaleidoscope the image is not structured into segments, but is more free form.

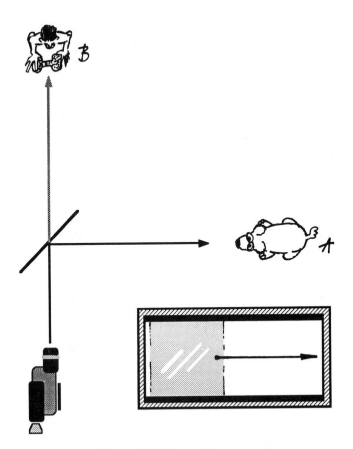

Figure 75 Mirror wipe set-up.

(a)

(b)

Figure 76 (a) Multiple mirror kaleidoscope on simple title. (b) Multiple mirror kaleidoscope on a more complex image.

Two way mirrors

Semi-silvered mirrors can be bought from mirror resilvering works. These have a very thin transparent protective layer applied to the half-strength aluminium 'silvering' to prevent tarnishing. Sometimes they are mounted with another plain piece of glass bound to the silvered side for mechanical protection. These are rather expensive but a cheaper version can be obtained by asking for a thin layer of silvering and no protective backing or mounting. This will tarnish in time but can be resilvered again. For accurate work have the mirror made from float glass. This is not optically flat but will suffice for many applications.

Figure 77 Mirror tube effect on simple title.

Effects using two-way mirrors rely on changing the light levels on the two scenes. The set-up is as in Figure 75, the mirror wipe, but now the mirror is static and the scenes have to be able to be independently lit with no spill-over of light onto each other.

Scene A is fully lit while scene B is in darkness. The audience only sees scene A. As the illumination is increased on scene B it becomes visible. The illumination is simultaneously lowered on scene A and a complete transition is made. There are also interesting things to be done at the half-way stages. Ghosts, text, diagrams can all be made to appear and disappear in certain parts of scene A by fading the lighting up and down on scene B.

Title on mirrors

Figure 78 shows a sequence of titles for a video on kosher food. The director wanted to involve and introduce the presenter in the titling sequence to put a face to what was to be mostly a voice-over. He cut the title from black paper and stuck it to the top of an old dress mirror that reflected the plain background. At first the audience only sees the plain colour of the featureless background and there is nothing to suggest a mirror is in use. The camcorder now zooms back and the title appears. Because there is no clue in

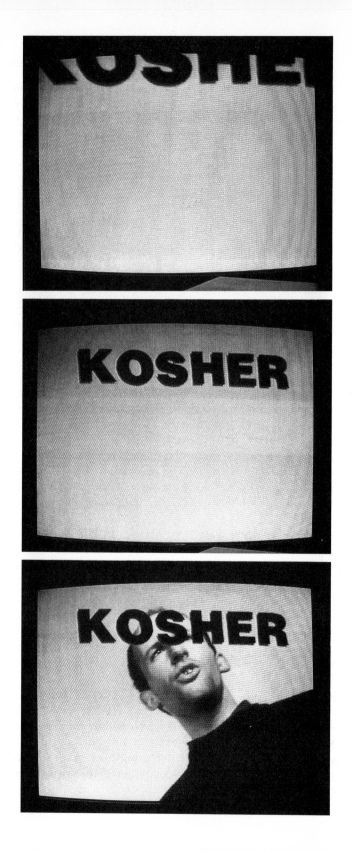

Figure 78 'Kosher' title sequence.

the featureless background that the camera is zooming out it appears to the audience that the title swoops in over the top of the frame and comes to rest a metre or so away. At this point the presenter moves so that his reflection is seen and talks to camera via the mirror. Because the audience cannot, and have not, seen the presenter directly they are not aware that it is a reflection. A little rehearsal was necessary to get the angles and eyelines right and it took five takes to get an acceptable version.

Anamorphic mirrors

An anamorphic mirror is simply a cylindrical mirror, or a section from a cylinder. It is possible to make one using the metallized melinex sheet used for the mirror tube but it tends to be too flimsy and is liable to fall over at the crucial moment.

A more robust solution is to use a flawless aluminium or chrome-plated tube. The size used for the effect in Figure 81 is 30 mm diameter by 200 mm long. The aluminium tube has to be polished to a high degree of finish using a normal household metal polish.

The artwork has to be prepared ready distorted so that the mirror will reflect it correctly. This is done using the grids in Figure 80. First: draw the shape or text you wish to use on the conventional rectangular grid. I suggest you make a photocopy of these grids. Second: copy the drawing square by square onto a piece of thin layout or tracing paper laid over the circular grid. Add any fine details by freehand while checking in the mirror. Finally check with the mirror that all is well.

Figure 79 'Kosher' title sequence set-up.

Anamorphic mirrors respond well to movement on a turntable or by being placed in shot to resolve the hitherto confusing graphics.

The finer you make the grids, the more accurately you will be able to transfer the original.

Out of focus

This is a very simple but effective technique. Choose an object which has some specular highlights, such as a dew-dropped plant, a piece of cut glass or a piece of crumpled aluminium baking foil. Frame and focus this in the viewfinder at close distance then turn the focus to infinity so that the object is totally out of focus and all that can be seen are some strange swirls of light.

It is most effective when the specular highlights are against a dark background. Colour can be very effective, added as a filter or two either over the camcorder or over any light source.

Fluid ripple

Set text or illustration in waterproof ink and further protect with matt varnish, on a sheet of acrylic or plastic laminate such as formica, or plastic paper.

Sink this in a shallow dish such as a photographic processing dish and place on a copystand. Cover with water. Light and agitate the surface of the water appropriately. Take care! Camcorders, lights, electricity and water do not go well together.

Variations on this theme include using a clear acrylic dish with underlighting, coloured water/lights, using cooking oil instead of water, adding fish . . .

Graffiti

These are very popular for urban decay, football, drug abuse, police and similar social conscience videos. If you cannot find your graffiti ready made, and it is not often that you see your cast list or actual video title on the underpass walls, then you will have to do it yourself.

Get some A3 sheets of white blotting paper. Find a wall that has the sort of texture you want. Soak the blotting paper with water and push the sheet firmly against the wall with a very firm sponge or rounded cloth pad, pressing it into the texture. Immediately gently peel the blotting paper off and lay it on a board to dry. It might be an idea to make two or three while you are here in case there are disasters later at the graffiti stage. When it is dry spray the surface lightly with matt varnish such as Ronseal or Letracote matt. This will seal the blotting paper and allow you to paint it with a brush without the surface breaking up or wetting it so much that the texture smooths out.

Now for the actual graffiti. Do not use full-size aerosol cans as they give too big a spray pattern. Instead use modeller's spray colours in small aerosols. Practise on some scrap paper first. Do not try to get it too perfect; it should look free and anarchic!

Melting and dissolving captions

There are several varieties of this technique. You can choose to have the entire caption burst into flames, selected parts (the burning trail of destruction across the country) or just the illustrative or text matter.

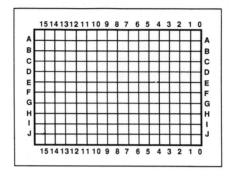

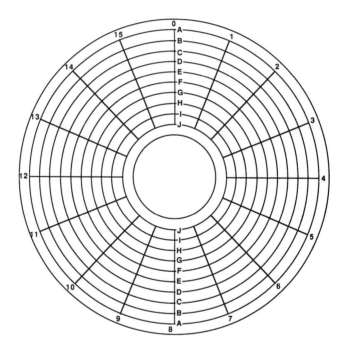

(a)

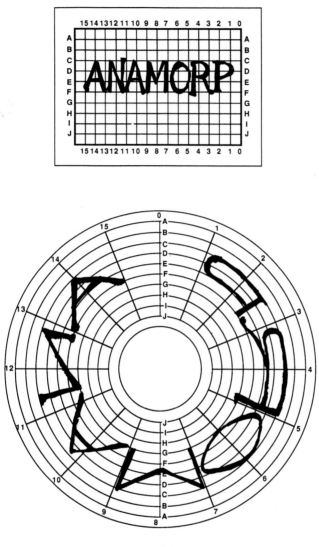

(b)

Figure 80 (a) Anamorphic mirror transfer grids. (b) Text set-up on grid.

Figure 81 Effect of anamorphic mirror.

The first is quite easy to do, just set light to it. But do work outdoors, protect yourself and the camcorder and have a bucket of water handy. Huge fires are unnecessary; a small burner such as a propane canister torch will give you the necessary control. Apply this to the back or an unseen edge. Make colour photocopies of the original and set light to these while supporting them on something fireproof.

Having a selected part smoulder needs a little preparation before hand. When the caption is complete mix up a concentrated solution of saltpetre (nitre) in water. Paint this over or behind the areas you wish to burn. Leave it to dry. Light the end of the trail with something smouldering. The fire will burn its away along it fairly precisely. It's very gentle. In fact it is so gentle that it makes a very good continuous action backdrop to the whole set of titles.

Burning the text only is a little trickier. Figure 83 shows a method of burning instant lettering. Of course, any flammable letterform will do, the important thing is to control the amount and the direction of the heat. Do not be tempted to think this could be done on a domestic cooker as the vertical camera angle could result in an unpleasant experience!

Instant lettering can be melted very easily with cellulose thinners. Set the lettering on a sheet of glass or metal and gently pour the thinners over. Take great care, as cellulose thinners are **very** inflammable. Work well away from naked lights. The fumes are rather pervasive too, so work outdoors or in a well-ventilated room. Thinners can also damage the body of your camcorder, so keep your hands and working area clean and avoid splashes. Have fun!

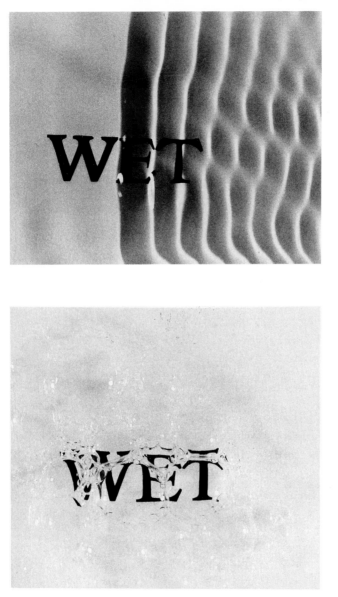

(a)

(b)

Figure 82 Effect of fluid ripple. (a) The word WET was set in instant lettering on the bottom of a white photographic dish. Water was poured in and gently moved about. (b) A few drops of washing-up liquid gave the bubbles.

Figure 83 Burning captions.

C&G Suppliers List

3M

3M House, PO Box 1,
Bracknell, Berks RG12 1BR.
Phone 0344 58477   Telex
Fax   Cable

Suppliers of
A/V, Graphic, OHP products and Scotch™
Self Adhesive Tapes etc.

Ademco Drimount Ltd

Coronation Road, Cressex Industrial Estate,
High Wycombe, Bucks. HP12 3TA
Phone 0494 448661   Telex
Fax   Cable

Suppliers of
Dry mounting and laminating equipment and
materials.

Aico International

Aico House, Faraday Road,
Newbury, Berks. RG13 2AD
Phone 0635 49797   Telex
Fax   Cable

Suppliers of
Silk Tripods, Hama photo and video
equipment (Videocut 10 & 20 Video editors)
Paximat projectors, Aico photo accessories.

Apple Computer UK Ltd

Eastman Way,
Hemel Hempstead, Herts. HP2 7QH
Phone 0442 60244   Telex 825834 APPLUK G

Suppliers of
Apple Macintosh Plus, MacII, AppleIIE,
Laserwriters and a host of associated goodies.
Also Hypercard Software.

Berol Ltd

Oldmeadow Road,
King's Lynn, Norfolk PE30 4JR
Phone 0553 761221   Telex 817409
Fax 0553 766534   Cable

Suppliers of
A wide range of designers' pens and pencils.

3P Paint Company (Stockport) Ltd

Hallam Mill, Hallam Street,
Stockport SK2 6PT
Phone 061 480 1233   Telex
Fax 061 477 0561   Cable

Suppliers of
Specialist paints and clear lacquers. Will make
up small amounts to individual requirements.

Agfa-Gevaert Ltd

27 Great West Road,
Brentford, Middlesex TW8 9AX
Phone 081 560 2131   Telex
Fax   Cable

Suppliers of
Photographic materials and equipment.
AgfaLith film.

Antex (Electronics) Ltd

2 Westbridge Industrial Estate,
Tavistock, Devon PL19 8DE
Phone 0822 613656   Telex 9312110595 AE G
Fax 0822 617598   Cable

Suppliers of
Soldering irons and equipment manufacturers

Arquati (UK) Ltd

2 Wolseley Road,
Kempston, Bedford MK42 7AY
Phone 0234 857488   Telex 826973 ARQBED G

Suppliers of
Picture frame mouldings, ready-made frames
and a very wide range of mounting boards,
including foam boards.

Bollom J.W.

PO Box 78, Croydon Road,
Beckenham, Kent BR3 4BL
Phone 081 650 9171   Telex 946804
Fax   Cable

Suppliers of
Bromel display felts, materials and PVC of a
great variety of surfaces.

Bush & Meissner Ltd

PO Box 145
Radlett, Herts. WD7 7BS
Phone 0903 858288   Telex
Fax 0903 858386   Cable

Suppliers of
Photographic studio accessories and
equipment such as copystands, lighting,
lightboxes etc.

Chartpak

Station Road,
Didcot, Oxfordshire OX11 7NB
Phone 0235 812607   Telex 837339
Fax 0235 813801   Cable

Suppliers of
Graphic, engineering and office products.
Dry transfer lettering, symbols, tapes and
markers. American, some unusual products.

Chequers (UK) Ltd

1–4 Christina Street,
London EC2A 4PA
Phone 071 739 6964   Telex 291673 GLARE
Fax 071 729 6630   Cable

Suppliers of
Polarizing sheet filters for rostrum, copy
camera or animation lights. Filter screens for
VDU computer displays.

Climpex Ltd

Hammers Lane, Mill Hill,
London NW7 4DY
Phone 081 959 1060   Telex
Fax   Cable

Suppliers of
Small stands and clamps for holding models,
props etc.

Como Drills

The Mill, Mill Lane, Worth,
Deal, Kent CT14 0PA
Phone 0304 612132   Telex 96149 MODEL G
Fax 0304 614696   Cable

Suppliers of
Como geared motors, miniature electric drills
and sanders for model makers.

Cromatek Optical Effects Filters

Local camera and photographic suppliers.
Phone   Telex
Fax   Cable

Suppliers of

CF Cases

31 Consul Road,
Rugby, Warwickshire CV21 1PB
Phone 0788 535484   Telex 312242 MIDTLX G
Fax 0788 70933   Cable

Suppliers of
Robust flight cases for delicate equipment.

Checkmate Digital Ltd

80 Mildmay Park,
London N1 4PR
Phone 071 923 0658
Fax 071 254 1655

Suppliers of
HAM-E 24bit graphics enhancement for
Amiga computers.

Chromacolour Animation Supplies

Cartoon House, 27/29 Whitfield Street,
London W1P 5RB
Phone 071 636 2103   Telex 298668
Fax 071 436 4678   Cable

Suppliers of
Paints, cells, pin bars, prepunched animation
paper, video animation controllers, graphic
materials.

Coated Specialities Ltd

Calder Way, Horton Road,
Colnbrook, Berks. SL3 0BQ
Phone 0753 685700   Telex 847189
Fax 0753 685410   Cable

Suppliers of
Morane^{TM} document and card laminating
systems.

Cow Proofings Ltd

Eastbourne Road,
Slough, Berks. SL1 4SF
Phone 0753 22274   Telex
Fax 0753 691952   Cable

Suppliers of
Cow gum rubber adhesive and litho printing
blankets.

Cumberland Pencil Co.

Southey Works,
Keswick, Cumbria CA12 5NG
Phone 07687 72116   Telex
Fax   Cable

Suppliers of
Genuine British pencils.

Daler-Rowney

Southern Industrial Area, PO Box 10,
Bracknell, Berks. RG12 4ST
Phone 0344 424621   Telex 847618
Fax 0344 486511   Cable

Suppliers of
Mounting board, card and papers for captions
and video graphics, art materials, Doc
Martin's colours and waterproof.

Draka Polva (UK) Ltd

131a Moss Lane, Hale,
Altrincham, Cheshire WA15 8BY
Phone 061 941 5161   Telex 668749
Fax 061 928 5307   Cable

Suppliers of
Plastic sheeting.

Dynamic Graphics (UK) Ltd

Media House, Eastways Industrial Estate,
Witham, Essex CM8 3YJ
Phone 0376 516006   Telex 987545 (DG UK)
Fax 0376 518878   Cable

Suppliers of
Clip art on disc and hard copy.

Electrovalue Ltd (Northern Branch)

680 Burnage Lane,
Manchester M19 1NA
Phone 061 432 4945   Telex
Fax 061 432 4127   Cable

Suppliers of
Electrical and electronic components and kits.

EMA Model Supplies Ltd

58–60 The Centre,
Feltham, Middlesex TW13 4BH
Phone 081 890 5270
Telex 263439 EMALON G
Fax   Cable

Suppliers of
Wide range of modelmaking supplies plus
architectural and interior design components.
Como 6 V DC geared motors.

DeVilbiss

Ringwood Road, Northbourne,
Bournemouth, Dorset BH11 9LH
Phone 0202 571111   Telex
Fax   Cable

Suppliers of
Airbrushes and general spraying equipment
with many applications.

Durst (UK) Ltd

Felstead Road, Longmead Ind. Est.,
Epsom, Surrey KT19 9AR
Phone 03727 26262   Telex 24593
Fax 03727 40761   Cable

Suppliers of
Professional photographic equipment,
processors, enlargers, etc. Amateur
equipment distributed by Johnsons'
Photopia.

Edding C.W. (UK) Ltd

North Orbital Trading Estate,
Napsbury Lane, St Albans, Herts AL1 1XQ
Phone 0727 34471   Telex
Fax 0727 39970   Cable

Suppliers of
Felt and fibre tipped pens, rules, markers,
stencils etc.

Electrovalue Ltd

28 St. Judes Road, Englefield Green,
Egham, Surrey TW20 0HB
Phone 0784 433603   Telex
Fax 0784 435216   Cable

Suppliers of
Electrical and electronic components and kits.

Excelsior Containers (Bury) Ltd

Ferngrove Mills, Rochdale Old Road,
Bury, Lancs. BL9 7LS
Phone 061 797 0855   Telex
Fax   Cable

Suppliers of
Aluminium and rigid protective equipment
cases.

Film Sales Ltd

145 Nathan Way, Woolwich Industrial Estate,
London SE28 0BR
Phone 081 311 2000
Telex 896942 SHARET G
Fax   Cable

Suppliers of
A very wide range of materials for film
animation, OHP, designers' drawing
materials, colours, acetates, register punched
paper etc.

Fotadvise (MEW) Ltd

22 Aylmer Court, Aylmer Road,
London N2 0BU
Phone 081 340 3820   Telex
Fax   Cable

Suppliers of
Marata rear projection screens (as used by the
BBC).

Fuji Photo Film (UK) Ltd

Fuji Film House, 125 Finchley Road,
London NW3 6JH
Phone 071 586 5900   Telex
Fax   Cable

Suppliers of
Fujicolour colour negative films, Fujichrome
colour transparency films and Neopan Black
and White film.

George Elliott & Sons Ltd

London Road,
Westerham, Kent TN16 1DR
Phone 0959 62198   Telex 95652
Fax 0959 64709   Cable

Suppliers of
BosScreen back-projection screen material
for video transfers. General AV and photo
equipment.

Gordon Harwood Computers,

New Street,
Alfreton, Derbyshire DE5 7BP
Phone 0773 836781
Fax 0773 831040

Suppliers of
Pro-Gen Amiga Genlocks. Spectracolor
drawing and animation control.

Focal Press

Borough Green,
Sevenoaks, Kent TN15 8PH
Phone 0732 884567   Telex 95678
Fax   Cable

Suppliers of
Books on all aspects of photography, video,
radio and film. Now a division of
Butterworths.

Foxall and Chapman Ltd

Unit 4, Downing Street Industrial Estate,
Charlton Place, Manchester M12 6HJ
Phone 061 274 4455   Telex
Fax   Cable

Suppliers of
Photographic materials and equipment,
including Screenphot photographic
aluminium.

Geliot Whitman

Herschell Road,
London SE23 1EQ
Phone 081 699 9262   Telex
Fax   Cable

Suppliers of
Typographic design and printers' equipment.

GH Smith and Partners (Sales) Ltd

Berechurch Road,
Colchester, CO2 7QH
Phone 0206 48221   Telex 987801
Fax   Cable

Suppliers of
Pelikan artists' materials, Plaka casein
emulsion for painting on celluloid and
Motivision Creativcolor OHP transparency
material.

Graphic Books International Ltd

PO Box 349, Rue des Goddards, Castel,
Guernsey, Channel Islands
Phone 0481 53125   Telex 4191246
Fax 0481 57089   Cable

Suppliers of
Fairburns Figures and a wide range of
graphics books.

Hanimex UK Ltd

AV Division, Hanimex House,
Faraday Road, Dorcan,
Swindon, Wilts.
Phone 0793 26211   Telex
Fax   Cable

Suppliers of
AV equipment, projectors, Graphic Writer.

Hegner (UK) Ltd

111 Sutton Road,
Southend, Essex SS2 5PB
Phone 0702 617298   Telex
Fax   Cable

Suppliers of
Fretsaws for intricate cutting of wood (up to
2″ thick), metal and plastics.

Heyden & Son Ltd

Spectrum House, Hillview Gardens,
London NW4 2JQ
Phone 081 203 5171
Telex 28303 HEYLDN G
Fax 081 203 1027   Cable

Suppliers of
Hot binding, comb binding, hot laminating
machines and materials.

Ilford

Christopher Martin Road,
Basildon, Essex SS14 3ET
Phone   Telex
Fax   Cable

Suppliers of
Photographic materials and equipment.

Johnsons Photopia

Hempstalls Lane,
Newcastle under Lyme ST5 0SW
Phone 0782 615131   Telex 36222
Fax 0782 619999   Cable

Suppliers of
Photographic equipment including the
smaller Durst enlargers and GePe slide
mounts.

K.R. Whiston Ltd

Bate Mill, New Mills,
Stockport SK12 4PT
Phone 0663 42028   Telex
Fax 0663 43071   Cable

Suppliers of
Engineer's supplies. Surplus and new
electromechanical equipment. Adhesives.
Tools. Wonderful catalogue.

Harkness Screen Supplies

The Gale Studios, Station Road,
Boreham Wood, Herts. WD6 1DQ
Phone 081 953 3611
Telex 8955602 PERLUX G
Fax 081 207 3627   Cable Screens London

Suppliers of
Front and rear projection screen materials.

Henkel Home Improvement and Adhesive Products

Winsford, Cheshire CW7 3QY
Phone   Telex
Fax   Cable

Suppliers of
Copydex latex adhesive and other adhesives.

ICI

Petrochemicals and Plastics Division,
Welwyn Garden City
Phone 07073 23400   Telex
Fax   Cable

Suppliers of
Perspex plastics and cement.

Instrument Plastics Ltd

5 Kings Grove Industrial Estate,
Maidenhead, Berks. SL6 4DP
Phone 0628 770018   Telex
Fax 0628 773299   Cable

Suppliers of
Polarizing filters for copy camera and
animation camera lights. Contact Richard
Lane.

JVC Professional Products (UK) Ltd

Alperton House, Bridgewater Road,
Wembley, Middx. HA0 1EG
Phone 081 902 8812   Telex
Fax 081 900 0941   Cable

Suppliers of
Video cameras, camcorders, videotape
recording equipment etc.

Kaiser (UK) Ltd

CCS Centre, Vale Lane, Bedminster,
Bristol BS3 5RU
Phone 0272 635263   Telex
Fax   Cable

Suppliers of
Photographic accessories, copystands,
product tables, enlargers etc.

Keith Johnson and Pelling

Promandis House, 19/21 Conway Street,
London W1P 5HL
Phone 071 380 1144
Telex 23364 PELCRO G
Fax 071 380 1135   Cable

Suppliers of
Bowens studio flash equipment and slide
duplicators. General photo dealers.

Kenro Photographic Products

The Oppenheimer Centre,
Greenbridge Road, Swindon,
Wilts. SN3 3LH
Phone 0793 615836   Telex 444726
Fax 0793 513561   Cable

Suppliers of
Photographic accessories, mounts, storage
systems etc.

Kodak

Swallowdale Lane,
Hemel Hempstead, Herts. HP2 7EY
Phone 0442 42281   Telex
Fax   Cable

Suppliers of
Photographic materials and equipment,
Kodalith film and developer. Supply centres
in Bristol, Birmingham, Manchester and
Glasgow.

KVP Ltd

Picadilly Mill, Lower Street,
Stroud, Gloucs GL5 2HT
Phone 0453 753891   Telex
Fax 0453 753892   Cable

Suppliers of
Video test charts for setting up video
equipment.

Letraset UK Ltd

195–203 Waterloo Road,
London SE1 8XJ
Phone 071 928 7551   Telex 917233
Fax   Cable

Suppliers of
Graphic products of great variety including
dry transfer lettering, DTP software and
graduated paper.

Kennet Engineering

The Lodge Works,
Drayton Parlsoe, Bucks. MK17 0JT
Phone 029672 605   Telex
Fax   Cable

Suppliers of
Benbo tripods (manufacturers).

Kentmere Ltd

Staveley,
Kendal, Cumbria LA8 9BP
Phone 0539 821365   Telex
Fax   Cable

Suppliers of
British photographic papers and very good
too.

Kroy (Europe) Ltd

Worton Grange,
Reading RG2 0LZ
Phone 0734 861411   Telex
Fax   Cable

Suppliers of
Dry transfer lettering machines.

Lastolite Ltd

8 Vulcan Court, Hermitage Industrial Estate,
Coalville, Leicestershire LE6 3FL
Phone 0530 35129
Telex 342351 TRANSO-G
Fax 0530 510156   Cable

Suppliers of
Photographic reflectors, white tents and
portable projection screens.

Lloyd Paton (LPM) Ltd

34 Moorfield Walk, Urmston,
Manchester M31 1TT
Phone 061 747 9949   Telex
Fax   Cable

Suppliers of
Educational suppliers of OHPs, shredders,
binders, spirit duplicators, screens,
transparency makers, stationery, professional
cassette recorders, plastic paper.

MacSoft

Bridge House, Unit 1,
Wellington, Somerset TA21 0AA
Phone 082 347 3625   Telex
Fax   Cable

Suppliers of
Software for Macintosh computers, especially
desk top publishing and clip art.

Marcam Ltd

62 Tenter Road, Moulton Park Business
Centre, Northampton NN3 1AX
Phone 0604 790466
Fax 0604 647403

Suppliers of
Accelerator boards, Rendale Genlocks.

May and Baker (M&B)

Raynham Road South,
Dagenham, Essex
Phone 081 592 3060   Telex
Fax   Cable

Suppliers of
Photographic chemicals, such as Novolith
Lith developer, Amfix fixer, Promicrol film
developer and Suprol paper developer.

Meadows and Passmore

Medmaw House, Farningham Road,
Crowborough, E. Sussex TN6 2JP
Phone 0892 662255   Telex
Fax 0892 662277   Cable

Suppliers of
Equipment, materials, tools and supplies for
clockmakers.

Microspot

London House, 5–11 London Road,
Maidstone, Kent ME16 8HR
Phone 062 268 7771   Telex
Fax   Cable

Suppliers of
Software for Macintosh computers, especially
desk top publishing and clip art.

Mike Sweetland Lighting Ltd

44 Higher Ardwick,
Manchester M12 6DA
Phone 061 273 4003/4   Telex
Fax   Cable

Suppliers of
Rosco Cinegel products, lighting diffusers,
smoke generators, video lighting kits, etc.

Maplin

PO Box 3,
Rayleigh, Essex SS6 8LR
Phone 0702 552911   Telex 995695
Fax   Cable

Suppliers of
Electronic components, equipment and kits.
Branches in many large towns.

Martelec Ltd

43 Queen's Road,
Farnborough, Hants. GU14 6JP
Phone 0252 515666   Telex
Fax   Cable

Suppliers of
Electronic components.

Maze Technology

Zenith House, 210 Church Road, Leyton,
London E10 7JQ
Phone 081 556 5620

Suppliers of
Amiga and PC based computer graphics,
titling, video effects, genlocks, PAL encoders
and frame grabbers.

Mecanorma Ltd

10 School Road,
London NW10 6TD
Phone 081 961 6565
Telex 926079 MNORMA G
Fax 081 961 5313   Cable

Suppliers of
Beautiful range of products from instant
lettering to airbrushes and compressors. Clip
art dry transfer sheets too.

Mike Allen Distribution Co. Ltd

10 Parsons Green, Boulton Road,
Stevenage, Herts SG1 4QG
Phone 0438 367787   Telex
Fax 0438 367597   Cable

Suppliers of
UK distributors of B+W filters, Stitz tripods,
Tenba bags, Tetenal chemicals.

Model Shop

209 Deansgate,
Manchester M3 3NW
Phone 061 834 3972   Telex
Fax   Cable

Suppliers of
Modelmakers' tools and equipment. Also
ready-made kits, small engines and electric
motors.

Multicore

Kelsey House, Wood Lane End,
Hemel Hempstead, Herts. HP2 4RQ
Phone 0442 233233   Telex
Fax 0442 69554   Cable

Suppliers of
Solder and flux.

Omnicrom Systems Ltd

Tonge Bridge Way,
Bolton BL2 6BD
Phone 0204 392050   Telex 635692
Fax 0204 35165   Cable

Suppliers of
Colour and reversed-out OHP transparency-making equipment.

Optex Ltd

22/26 Victoria Road,
New Barnet, Herts. EN4 9PF
Phone 081 441 2199
Telex 8955869 OPTEX G
Fax 081 449 3646   Cable

Suppliers of
Studio and location accessories for film and video including Sachtler tripods and pedestal systems.

Optical Filters

Unit 36, Princess Estate, Summerleys Road,
Princes Risborough HP17 9PX
Phone 0844 274369   Telex
Fax 0844 274431   Cable

Suppliers of
Optical filters for VDU screens. Polarizing filter sheets.

Pandagraphic

426 Wakefield Road, Denby Dale,
Huddersfield HD8 8QD
Phone 0484 861651
Telex 51458 COMHUD G
Fax 0484 861622   Cable

Suppliers of
Wire-O 'spiral' binding systems for books, reports etc.

Photon Beard Ltd

18 The Brunswick Centre, Marchmont Street,
London WC1N 1AE
Phone 071 837 8647   Telex
Fax 071 278 2203   Cable

Suppliers of
Manufacturers and suppliers of photographic and video lighting equipment, lightboxes, masking frames etc.

Plasti-Dip

Rake Heath, London Road,
Petersfield, Hants. GU33 7NT
Phone 0730 894321   Telex 858623
Fax 0730 894446   Cable

Suppliers of
Liquid rubber coating with a host of uses.

Polaroid

Ashley Road,
St. Albans, Herts. AL1 5PR
Phone 0727 59191   Telex 263246
Fax 0727 69335   Cable

Suppliers of
Instant films and cameras. Palette computer graphic camera recorder.

Proops Distributors Ltd

Heybridge Estate, Castle Road,
London NW1 8TD
Phone 071 267 1718   Telex
Fax   Cable

Suppliers of
Electrical, mechanical and optical components and materials, small tools etc. Geared DC motors and motor speed controllers.

RCW Colour Slides

PO Box 4DL, 7a Livonia Street,
London W1A 4DL
Phone 071 437 2183/4   Telex
Fax   Cable

Suppliers of
Hard and soft edged slide masks for multiple projector effects. Specially prepared graphics slides.

Roscolab Ltd

Blanchard Works, Kangley Bridge Road,
Sydenham,
London SE26 5AQ
Phone 081 659 2300
Telex 895 3352 ROSLAB G
Fax 081 659 3153   Cable

Suppliers of
Colour filter gels for lights. Polarizing filters,
flexible mirror, fog machines, stage supplies.

Rötring

Rötring-werke Riepe KG, D-2000
Hamburg 54, Germany
Phone   Telex
Fax   Cable

Suppliers of
Technical drawing pens. Available from all
good artist's suppliers.

Shand Higson & Co. Ltd

Taylor Street Industrial Estate,
Liverpool L5 5AD
Phone 051 207 5661   Telex
Fax   Cable

Suppliers of
SHC adhesive tapes.

Simmon Sound and Vision

28a Manor Row,
Bradford, W. Yorks.
Phone 0274 307763   Telex
Fax   Cable

Suppliers of
Cases, fluid head tripods, general AV
equipment.

Sony (UK) Ltd (Head Office)

Pipers Way, Thatcham,
Newbury, Berks. RG13 4LZ
Phone 0784 467000   Telex
Fax   Cable

Suppliers of
Audio and video equipment for professional
and domestic applications. Video8.

Specialist Lamp Distributors

1 Bradstone Road,
Manchester M8 8PH
Phone 061 831 7966   Telex
Fax   Cable

Suppliers of
All sorts of strange and conventional bulbs
for all sorts of equipment.

Rose H.S.

99 Seymour Grove, Old Trafford,
Manchester M16 0ND
Phone 061 872 3399   Telex
Fax   Cable

Suppliers of
Bienfang foam core board. Paper and boards.

Science Photo Library

112 Westbourne Grove,
London W2 5RU
Phone 071 727 4712   Telex
Fax 071 727 6041   Cable

Suppliers of
Photographs concerned with all aspects of
science and technology.

Signs & Labels Ltd

Corrie House, Corrie Way, Bredbury
Industrial Park, Stockport, Cheshire SK6 2ST
Phone 061 494 6125   Telex 666659 SIGNS G
Fax 061 430 8514   Cable

Suppliers of
Adhesive tapes, dispensers and labels of great
variety and application.

Solvit Plastic Binding Co. Ltd

Presentation House, St. George's Road,
Aldershot, Hants. GU12 4LF
Phone 0252 313431   Telex
Fax   Cable

Suppliers of
Hot glue, comb, staple binding systems.
Paper drills etc.

Staedtler (UK) Ltd

Pontyclun, Mid Glamorgan CF7 8YJ
Phone 0443 222421   Telex 497025
Fax 0443 237440   Cable

Suppliers of
A wide range of drafting equipment and
materials.

Supreme Magic Co.

64 High Street,
Bideford, Devon EX39 2AN
Phone 02372 79266   Telex
Fax   Cable

Suppliers of
Magic equipment including feather bouquets,
appearing cane and large stage items.

Swann Morten Ltd

Penn Works, Owlerton Green,
Sheffield S6 2BJ
Phone 0742 344231
Telex 547538 SWANN G
Fax   Cable

Suppliers of
Scalpels and knives.

The Bearing Mart Ltd

3–15 Barton Street, off Liverpool Road,
Manchester M3 4NN
Phone 061 832 3836   Telex
Fax   Cable

Suppliers of
A very wide range of ball and needle bearings,
thrust races, bushes etc.

The Perforated Front Projection Screen Co., Ltd

182 High Street,
Cottenham, Cambridge CB4 4RX
Phone 0954 50139   Telex
Fax   Cable

Suppliers of
All forms and sizes of front and rear
projection screens. Also cinema and theatre
furnishers and equipment suppliers.

Unicol

Unicol Engineering, Green Road,
Headington, Oxford OX3 8EU
Phone 0865 66000   Telex
Fax   Cable

Suppliers of
Very robust equipment stands and trolleys.

Vinten Broadcast Ltd

Western Way,
Bury St. Edmunds IP33 3TB
Phone 0284 752121
Telex 81176 VINTEN G
Fax 0284 750560   Cable

Suppliers of
Video and cine camera tripods and
mountings.

Swan Stabilo Ltd

74 Buckingham Avenue,
Slough, Berks. SL1 4PA
Phone 0753 821941   Telex 847829 SWAN G
Fax 0753 691317   Cable
Suppliers of
Pens, markers, pencils and OHP materials in
great profusion.

Techprint Lettering Systems Ltd

International House, Windmill Road,
Sunbury on Thames TW16 7HR
Phone 0932 789863   Telex
Fax   Cable

Suppliers of
Midas Express lettering machines.

The Milliput Company

Unit 5, Marian Mawr Industrial Estate,
Dolgellau, Wales LL40 1UU
Phone 0341 422562   Telex
Fax   Cable

Suppliers of Milliput epoxy modelling putty.

Transtar

Victoria Industrial Estate, Victoria Road,
W. Hebburn, Tyne & Wear NE31 1UB
Phone 0632 832797   Telex Transtar 537234
Fax   Cable

Suppliers of
Lighting control equipment. Flourescent tube
starters and ballast all in one.

Videocopy

3 Buslingthorpe Green, Meanwood Road,
Leeds LS27 2HG
Phone 0532 625650   Telex
Fax   Cable

Suppliers of
Video duplication from any standard to any
standard. Also standards conversion to or
from PAL NTSC or SECAM.

Wiggins Teape Paper Ltd

Keays House, Granby Avenue,
Birmingham B33 0SX
Phone 021 783 9931
Telex 858031 WTBSTK G
Fax   Cable

Suppliers of
Colorama Background Paper. General paper
manufacturers.

Winsor & Newton

Whitefriars Avenue,
Harrow, Middx. HA3 5RH
Phone 081 427 4343
Telex 927295 ARTIST G
Fax 081 863 7177   Cable

Suppliers of
Artists' and designers' equipment and
materials. Coloured inks, acrylic water
colours.

Index

Acetate sheets, 9–10, 48
Adhesive, contact; cow gum; spray;
    water based; Uhu, 46–7
Adhesive reveal effects, 83–4
Anamorphic mirrors, 103–4, 106–8
Animated card graphics, 61–5, 66, 67
Animatics, 90–1
Apple Macintosh computer, 34
Auto white balance, 10–11

Backlighting, drum titlers, 80
Balanced direct light, 3, 6–7
Barn doors, lights with, 5, 6
Belt titlers, 50–1, 52–4
Blick lettering, 34
Blow away effects, 83–4
Books, page turning, 51, 55, 58–9
Brushes, sable hair; hog hair; bristle, 39
Burning captions, 105, 108
Burnishers, 40

Calliope typeface, 31, 33
Camcorders,
    auto white balance, 10–11
    clean starts and noiseless breaks, 90
    colour rendering, 24–5
    Hi8, 24, 91
    light levels, 4
    with part colour filters, 93
    start-stop timing, 90
    S-VHS, 24
    titling memory, 9
Cameras, SLR, 16–17
Captions,
    rotating, 65–82
    sand and powder, 83–4
Caption stands, 20–1
CCD chip, videocamera, 24–5
Cellulose lacquers, 93
Chroma noise, 24–5
Colour, 24–7
    balance, 10–11
    circle, 25–7
    cultural perceptions, 25–7
    moods engendered by, 25–7
    problems with video cameras, 24–5
Colour gels, use of, 15–16
Compasses, 43

Computers, Apple Macintosh, 34
Contrast, 27
Copy lighting, 3–10
Copyright, 18, 49
Copystands, 21–3
Correcting fluid, 47
Crouzet mains motor, 65
Cube titlers, 81–2
Cutting boards, 40

Designer's gouache paint, 47
Diffused direct light, 3, 5
Diffusion filters, 92–3, 94–5
Directional lighting, 7–10, 84
Discs, titling, 77
Dissolving captions, 105, 108
Drawing boards, 41
Drawing instruments, 42–9
Drum titlers, 50, 78–81

Electrically powered turntables, 65,
    68–77
Erasers, 43
Exposure, copy lighting, 7
Exposure methods, 10–11

Fantasy Dip-it film, 93
Film, for video screen copying, 17
Filters, 92–7
    Cokin and Cromatek range, 92
    diffusion, 16, 92–3, 94–5
    multiple image, 93–6
    part colour, 93
    polarizing, 11–12
    star, 96–7
Fluid ripple, 105, 109
Focus, out of focus effects, 104
Freeze frame, 17, 18

Ghosts, 101
Glare, 4, 12
Glowing effects, 15
Graffiti, 105
Grammer, graphics, 28
Graphics equipment and materials, 39–
    49
Grids, 28–30
Guillotines, blade; rotary, 43–4

Halation, 4
Hi8 camcorders, 24, 91

Illustrations, videoing, 37–9
Inclinometer, 17, 19
Indirect light, 3, 4, 6–7
Inks, 47

Kaleidoscopes, 98, 100
Knives, 44

Lacquers, for glass and acrylic surfaces,
    93
Letraset lettering, 34
Lettering methods, 34–6
Letter spacing, 36
Lighting,
    captions, 56
    copy, 3–10
    directional, 7–10
    indirect, diffused and balanced, 3–7
Lights,
    tungsten halogen redhead, 6
    video, 6

Magnetic captions and charts, 57, 59–
    60
Mecanorma lettering, 34
Melting captions, 105, 108
Mirrors, 97–104
    anamorphic, 103–4
    Kaleidoscope, 98, 100
    titles on, 101–3
    tube, 98, 101
    two way, 100–1
Mirror wipe, 98, 99
Models, 89
Moiré interference patterns, 16, 37
Mood and colour, 25–7
Motors, electric,
    barbecue spit, 72
    battery powered, 69–74
    Crouzet mains, 65
    reduction gears, 69, 72–3
    reversing, 69, 70
    stepper, 74
Multiple images, 93–6

Opticals, 90–109
Overlays, acetate, 14

Paint, 47–8
Paper, requirements for video, 48–9
Paper engineering, 60–1

Pelikan Plaka paint, 47–8
Pencils, 45
Pens, 45
Photographing video screens, 16–19
Pivots, for paper, 61–4, 66, 67
Plastic paper, use of, 14
Playbill typeface, 31, 33
Polarizing filters, 11–12
Powder captions, 83–4
Proportions, video artwork, 28–30
Pugwash animation technique, 60

Reflections, unwanted, 12
Rolling rulers, 45–6
Rotating captions, 65–82

Sand captions, 83–4
Scalpels, 44
Scrolling effects, 50–1, 52–4
Shades, 27
Slatted belt titlers, 50–1, 52–4
Slide projectors, use of, 15
Sliders, 85–8
    reveal, 86
    universal, 87–8
Slides, 35 mm, copying, 14–15
Smearing, colour, 24–5
Sony CCD V800 Hi8 camcorder, 91
Stanley knives, 44
Star filters, 96–7
Straight edges, 40–1
Style consistency, 28
Sunlight, copy lighting with, 3, 4
S-VHS format, 24

Textures, 27
Three-dimensional effects, 10
Tide wash effects, 83
Times Roman typeface, 31
Tints, 27
Titlers,
    cube, 81–2
    disc, 77
    drum, 78–81
    mechanical, 50–1, 52–4
    models, 89
    perspex drum, 75
    sliders for, 85–8
    turntables, 65, 68–77
    vane, 82
    Velcro boards, 88
Transparencies, copying, 14–16
Tripods, 17
T-squares, 42

Turntables, 65, 68–77
  construction, 74–7
Typefaces, 30–4
  application suitability, 31–4
Typesetting methods, 34–6

U-Matic type record and playback, 91
Umbrellas, as light reflectors, 6–7

Vacuum table, 12, 13
Vane titlers, 82
Velcro boards, titling with, 88
Video camcorders *see* Camcorders
Video definition, 37
Video lights, 6
Video screens, photographing, 16–19

Xylene-based lacquers, 93